SALE NUMBER 4510M

DANCE • THEATER • OPERA • MUSIC HALL

Costume & Decor Designs, Photographs, Posters & Books

Including

Robert Edmond Jones' design for the decor of *Till Eulenspiegel* and other productions
25 designs by Chagall for *Aleko, 1942*
Léon Bakst, *Oedipus at Colonna,* Design for Theseus, 1903
Léon Bakst, *La Belle au Bois Dormant,* Design for the *Fiancé Indien, 1922*
Alexandre Benois, *David,* Design for the decor, 1928
Eugene Berman, *Amahl and the Night Visitors,* Design for the decor, 1952
Alexandra Exter, *Les Equivoques d'Amour,* Costume design, c. 1933
Alfred Edward Chalon, The celebrated *Pas de Quatre,* 1845
A photograph of Nijinsky in *Le Festin* signed by Nijinsky, 1909
An album of photographs of Pavlova by Malvina Hoffman, c. 1915

EXHIBITION
Saturday, December 13, 1980 from 10 a.m. to 5 p.m.
Sunday, December 14, 1980 from 1 p.m. to 5 p.m.
Monday, December 15, 1980 from 10 a.m. to 5 p.m.
Tuesday, December 16, 1980 from 10 a.m. to 5 p.m.
Wednesday, December 17, 1980 from 10 a.m. to 3 p.m.

PUBLIC AUCTION
Thursday, December 18, 1980 at 2:00 p.m.

For further information about this sale
please contact Hermine Chivian-Cobb
212/472-4764 and 472-4765

SOTHEBY PARKE BERNET INC.
980 Madison Avenue (76-77th Streets)
New York 10021 (212) 472-3400
Cable: Parkgal, New York
Telex: New York 232643 (SOL UR)

Cover Illustration: 86
Back Cover Illustration: 74

Sotheby Parke Bernet Inc · New York

ADMINISTRATION

Chairman & President
John L. Marion, 472-3426
Chief Operating Officer
Frederick H. Scholtz, 472-4862
Finance & Administration
Arnold M. Kagan, 472-3434
Special Sales & Real Estate
Edward Lee Cave, 472-3431
Client Services
C. Hugh Hildesley, 472-3454

Director of Sales, Fine Arts
David J. Nash, 472-3590
Marketing and Communications
Nancy Tremaine, 472-3424
Director of Sales, Decorative Arts
Robert C. Woolley, 472-3503
Marketing and Sales Coordination York Avenue Galleries
David N. Redden, 472-4669
Painting Departments Director
Mary-Anne Martin, 472-4766

Finance
Alan M. Forster, 472-3443
Treasurer
Diana D. Brooks, 472-3681
Controller
Howard Weiss, 472-3441
Regional Operations
John D. Block, 472-3568
Director of Sales, Jewelry
Dennis J. Scioli, 472-3421

Director of Sales, Books, Coins and Stamps
Jerry E. Patterson, 472-4703
Assistant to the President
Nancy A. Forster, 472-3426
General Counsel & Secretary
Mitchell Zuckerman, Esq.
472-3476
Museum Services
Susan L. Brody, 472-3478
Human Resources
Varian Ayers, 472-4721

EXPERT DEPARTMENTS

American Decorative Arts & Furniture
William W. Stahl, Jr., 472-3511
American Folk Art
Nancy Druckman, 472-3512
American Indian, African & Oceanic Art
Ellen Napiura, 472-3522
American Paintings
Peter B. Rathbone
Grete Meilman, 472-3551
Antiquities
Richard M. Keresey, 472-3521
Arms and Armour
David Wille, 472-3507
Art Deco
Eric Silver, 472-3509
Art Nouveau
Barbara E. Deisroth, 472-3508
Books & Manuscripts
David G. Park, 472-3593
Thomas P. Clarke
Chinese Art
James J. Lally, 472-3516
Chinese Paintings
Paula Gasparello, 472-3529

Coins
Jeremiah Brady, 472-4847
Collectibles (Toys, Dolls, Antique Clothing)
Pamela Brown, 472-4783
Contemporary Paintings, Drawings & Sculpture
Linda R. Silverman, 472-3543
English Furniture
Gerald Bland, 472-3513
European Furniture
Thierry Millerand, 472-3514
European & Chinese Export Porcelain
Letitia Roberts, 472-3517
European Works of Art, Ceramics, Pewter & Tapestries
David Wille, 472-3507
Impressionist & Modern Paintings
John L. Tancock, 472-3547
Islamic Works of Art, Miniatures & Manuscripts
Michael Jones, 472-3524

Japanese Art
D. Martin Lorber, 472-3525
Jewelry
Paul A. Russo, 472-3421
Jewelry (Antique)
Jacqueline Fay, 472-3422
Modern Paintings & Sculpture
Shary E. Grossman
Polly Rubin, 472-3545
Modern Drawings; Ballet & Theatre Arts
Hermine Chivian-Cobb, 472-4764
Musical Instruments
John Turner, 472-8443
19th Century European Paintings
Thilo von Watzdorf
Susan Bodo, 472-3537
19th Century Furniture
Margaret Caldwell, 472-3571
19th & 20th Century Latin American Paintings
Mary-Anne Martin, 472-4766
Old Master Paintings
Brenda J. Auslander, 472-3541

Paperweights
Lynne Tillman, 472-3506
Photographs
Anne Horton, 472-3595
Portrait Miniatures and Chess Sets
Sarah D. Coffin, 472-3532
Pre-Columbian Art
Claudia Giangola, 472-3575
Prints (Old Master)
Marc E. Rosen, 472-3437
Prints (19th & 20th Century)
Ruth M. Ziegler, 472-3437
Susan F. Pinsky, 472-3438
Rugs and Carpets
Michael B. Grogan, 472-3451
Russian Art
Gerard Hill, 472-3619
Silver, Vertu, Watches
Kevin L. Tierney, 472-3531
Snuff Bottles
Harold Stevens, Jr., 472-3529
Stamps
Andrew Levitt, (203) 743-4458
Vintage Vehicles
Chrys Landrigan, 472-4629

Assistant Controller
Arnold Aratoon, 472-4845
Assistant Treasurer
H. Garth Dickey, 472-3467
Administrative Services
Barbara Fischer, 472-3640
Advertising & Catalogue Production
Harriet F. Walley, 472-3415
Appraisals
Lauren Johnson, 472-3454
Art Transport Service
Ann Cook, 472-3468

ADMINISTRATIVE DEPARTMENTS

Bids and Sales Records
Madison Avenue Galleries
Roberta Louckx, 472-3450
York Avenue Galleries
Nancy Stahl, 794-3019
Catalogue Subscription
Helen F. Wellner, 472-3414
Credit and Billing
Madison Avenue Galleries
Lola Capel, 472-3461
York Avenue Galleries
Paul Cervino, 794-3027
Customer Advisory Service
Jane Wyeth, 472-3486
Customer Relations
Nancy Handy, 472-4727

Fine Arts Representative
Ruth Freudman, 472-4873
Estates Division
Samantha McIntosh, 472-4625
Exhibitions Decorator
Alfred Bristol, 472-3489
Facilities
Edward F. McGovern, 472-3491
Heirloom Discovery Day Coordinator
Mary Gera, 472-3503
International Office
Marjorie Crodelle, 472-4632
International Catalogue Sales & Bids
Wathena Slaughter, 472-3460

Inventory Control, Decorative Arts
Olivia Murray, 472-3501
Inventory Control, Paintings
Andrea Kust, 472-3535
Institutional Services
Robert D. Schonfeld, 472-3452
Newsletter & Publications
Betsy Pinover, 472-8458
Personnel
Cheryl Lincoln, 472-3479
Public Relations
Elizabeth Robbins, 472-4840
Special Client Services
Eunice S. Carroll, 472-3440

SALES CONDUCTED BY

Peter C. Wilson, C.B.E.   John L. Marion   Edward Lee Cave   C. Hugh Hildesley   David J. Nash   Robert C. Woolley
John D. Block   James J. Lally   Andrew Levitt   Marc E. Rosen   Dennis J. Scioli   William W. Stahl, Jr.   Eunice S. Carroll
Gerard J. Hill   Lorna C. Kelly   David N. Redden   Pamela Brown   Michael B. Grogan   Joseph Keiffer   Eric Silver

Admin. 12/80

CONDITIONS OF SALE

This catalogue, as amended by any posted notices or oral announcements during the sale, is Sotheby Parke Bernet Inc.'s and the Consignor's entire agreement with the purchaser relative to the property listed herein. The following Conditions of Sale, the Terms of Guarantee and any glossary contained herein are the complete and only terms and conditions on which all property is offered for sale. The property will be offered by us as agent for the Consignor, unless the catalogue indicates otherwise.

1. The authenticity of the Authorship of property listed in the catalogue is guaranteed as stated in the Terms of Guarantee; except as provided therein all property is sold "AS IS", and neither we nor the Consignor make any warranties or representations of the correctness of the catalogue or other description of the physical condition, size, quality, rarity, importance, provenance, exhibitions, literature or historical relevance of the property and no statement anywhere, whether oral or written, shall be deemed such a warranty or representation. Prospective bidders should inspect the property before bidding to determine its condition, size and whether or not it has been repaired or restored. We and the Consignor make no representation or warranty as to whether the purchaser acquires any reproduction rights in the property.

2. A premium of 10% of the successful bid price will be added thereto and is payable by the purchaser as part of the total purchase price.

3. We reserve the right to withdraw any property before sale.

4. Unless otherwise announced by the auctioneer, all bids are per lot as numbered in the catalogue.

5. We reserve the right to reject any bid. The highest bidder acknowledged by the auctioneer will be the purchaser. In the event of any dispute between bidders, or in the event of doubt on our part as to the validity of any bid, the auctioneer will have the final discretion either to determine the successful bidder or to reoffer and resell the article in dispute. If any dispute arises after the sale, our sale record is conclusive. Although in our discretion we will execute order bids or accept telephone bids as a convenience to clients who are not present at auctions, we are not responsible for any errors or omissions in connection therewith.

6. If the auctioneer decides that any opening bid is below the value of the article offered, he may reject the same and withdraw the article from sale, and if, having acknowledged an opening bid, he decides that any advance thereafter is insufficient, he may reject the advance.

7. On the fall of the auctioneer's hammer, title to the offered lot will pass to the highest bidder acknowledged by the auctioneer, subject to fulfillment by such bidder of all the conditions set forth herein, and such bidder thereupon (a) assumes full risk and responsibility therefor, (b) will sign a confirmation of purchase thereof, and (c) will pay the full purchase price therefor or such part as we may require. In addition to other remedies available to us by law, we reserve the right to impose a late charge of 1½% per month of the total purchase price if payment is not made in accordance with the conditions set forth herein. All property must be removed from our premises by the purchaser at his expense not later than 3 business days following its sale and, if it is not so removed, (i) a handling charge of 1% of the purchase price per month until its removal will be payable to us by the purchaser, with a minimum of 5% for any property not so removed within 60 days after the sale, and (ii) we may send the purchased property to a public warehouse for the account, risk and expense of the purchaser. If any applicable conditions herein are not complied with by the purchaser, in addition to other remedies available to us and the Consignor by law, including without limitation the right to hold the purchaser liable for the total purchase price, we at our option may either (a) cancel the sale, retaining as liquidated damages all payments made by the purchaser or (b) resell the property at public auction without reserve, and the purchaser will be liable for any deficiency, costs, including handling charges, the expenses of both sales, our commission on both sales at our regular rates, all other charges due hereunder and incidental damages. In addition, a defaulting purchaser will be deemed to have granted us a security interest in, and we may retain as collateral security for such purchaser's obligations to us, any property in our possession owned by such purchaser. We shall have all of the rights afforded a secured party under the New York Uniform Commercial Code with respect to such property and we may apply against such obligations all monies held or received by us for the account of, or due from us to, such purchaser. At our option, payment will not be deemed to have been made in full until we have collected funds represented by checks, or, in the case of bank or cashier's checks, we have confirmed their authenticity.

8. Lots marked with ■ immediately preceding the lot number are offered subject to a reserve, which is the confidential minimum price below which such lot will not be sold. We may implement such reserves by bidding on behalf of the Consignor. In certain instances, the Consignor may pay us less than the standard commission rate where a lot is "bought-in" to protect its reserve. Where the Consignor is indebted to or has a monetary guarantee from us, and in certain other instances, where we or our affiliated companies may have an interest in the offered lots and the proceeds therefrom other than our commissions, we may bid therefor to protect such interests.

9. Unless exempted by law, the purchaser will be required to pay the combined New York State and local sales tax or any applicable compensating use tax of another state on the total purchase price. The rate of such combined tax is 8% in New York City and ranges from 4% to 8% elsewhere in New York State.

10. These Conditions of Sale as well as the purchaser's and our respective rights and obligations hereunder shall be governed by and construed and enforced in accordance with the laws of the State of New York. By bidding at an auction, whether present in person or by agent, order bid, telephone or other means, the purchaser shall be deemed to have consented to the jurisdiction of the state courts of, and the federal courts sitting in, the State of New York.

11. We are not responsible for the acts or omissions of carriers or packers of purchased lots, whether or not recommended by us. Packing and handling of purchased lots by us is at the entire risk of the purchaser.

TERMS OF GUARANTEE

We guarantee the authenticity of Authorship of each lot contained in this catalogue on the terms and conditions set forth below.

1. Definition of Authorship

"Authorship" means the identity of the creator, the period, culture, source of origin of the property, as the case may be, as set forth in the **BOLD TYPE HEADING** of such catalogue entry.

2. Guarantee Coverage

Subject to the exclusions of (i) attributions of paintings, drawings or sculpture executed prior to 1870, and (ii) periods or dates of execution of the property, as explained in Paragraph 5 below, if within five (5) years from the date of the sale of any lot, the original purchaser of record tenders to us a purchased lot in the same condition as when sold through us and it is established that the identification of Authorship (as defined above) of such lot set forth in the **BOLD TYPE HEADING** of this catalogue description of such lot (as amended by any posted notices or oral announcements during the sale) is not substantially correct based on a fair reading of the catalogue including the terms of any Glossary contained herein, the sale of such lot will be rescinded and the original purchase price refunded.

3. Non-Assignability

It is specifically understood that the benefits of this Guarantee are not assignable and shall be applicable only to the original purchaser of the lot from us and not to the subsequent owners or others who have or may acquire an interest therein.

4. Sole Remedy

It is further specifically understood that the remedy set forth herein, namely the rescission of the sale and refund of the original purchase price paid for the lot, is exclusive and in lieu of any other remedy which might otherwise be available as a matter of law.

5. Exclusions

The Guarantee covers only the correctness of description of Authorship (as defined in 1 above) as identified in the **BOLD TYPE HEADING** of the catalogue item but does *not* extend to (i) the identity of the creator of paintings, drawings and sculpture executed before 1870 unless these works are determined to be counterfeits, as this is a matter of current scholarly opinion which can change, (ii) the identification of the periods or dates of execution of the property which may be proven inaccurate by means of scientific processes not generally accepted for use until after publication of the catalogue, or (iii) titles or other identification of offered lots or descriptions of physical condition and size, quality, rarity, importance, provenance, exhibitions and literature of historical relevance, which information normally appears in lower case type below the **BOLD TYPE HEADING** identifying the Authorship. Although our best judgment is used in attributing paintings, drawings and sculpture created prior to 1870 through the appropriate use of glossary terms, and due care is taken to insure the correctness of the supplemental material which appears below the **BOLD TYPE HEADING** of each entry in the catalogue, the Guarantee does not extend to any possible errors or omissions therein.

REMOVAL OF PROPERTY

Unless different arrangements have been agreed upon, all purchases must be removed by the buyer by 5 p.m. on the third business day following the sale. Purchases not so removed will be subject to a handling charge. See paragraph 7 of the "Conditions of Sale."

Clients are advised that packing and handling of purchased lots by our employees are undertaken solely as a courtesy for the convenience of clients; and in the case of fragile articles, will be undertaken at our sole discretion.

Although we recommend the use of professional packers, books and small articles which are not fragile can be packed on our premises, and, at our sole discretion, can be sent by mail or other carrier for a nominal charge. Prints and drawings in glazed frames cannot be handled in this manner. Charges for packing, insurance, and freight are payable by the purchaser. For further information: Miss Ann Cook, (212) 472-3468.

CS 5/80

ADVICE TO PROSPECTIVE BUYERS AND SELLERS

STANDARD COMMISSION RATES

Our standard commission for selling fine art property at auction is 10% of the successful bid price of each lot sold for more than $1000 and 15% of the successful bid price of each lot sold for $1000 or less, in either case together with an amount equal to the 10% premium paid by the buyer as part of the total purchase price.

BIDDING

Successful bidders attending the auction are required to sign a bid confirmation card upon the fall of the hammer and will not be permitted to take delivery of purchases until their checks have cleared unless they have previously established credit or made payment arrangements. A premium equal to 10% of the successful bid price will be added thereto and is payable by the buyer as part of the total purchase price.

As a convenience to clients who cannot attend a sale in person, Sotheby Parke Bernet will, if so instructed, execute written 'order bids' on their behalf, without additional cost. Order bidders should use the 'Bid Form' provided in the catalogue and note the 'Advice to Order Bidders' printed on each form. Telephone bids must be confirmed in writing or by cable. Sotheby Parke Bernet will not be responsible for errors or failure to execute bids.

Lots are bought for order bidders at the lowest possible price (which may be below the order bid price) subject to other bids and reserves. For further information: Mrs. Roberta Louckx, (212) 472-3450.

CATALOGUES AND PRICE LISTS

Catalogues, prepared by the expert departments involved, are published for all auction sales. These may be purchased singly or by annual subscription.

Printed lists recording the prices of all lots sold are also available. Single copies are $2.00 each.

The *Sotheby Parke Bernet Newsletter,* which lists sales held in New York, London, Los Angeles and elsewhere, is available for $3.00 per year ($5.00 overseas).

Catalogue subscription rates include the price lists and the *Newsletter.*

Catalogues, price lists, and detailed information on subscriptions are available at the galleries or by writing to the Subscription Department. (Please specify sale number when ordering.) For further information: Mrs. Helen F. Wellner, (212) 472-3414.

INSPECTION OF PROPERTY

You may bring your property (or photographs if the pieces are too large to carry) to either 980 Madison Avenue (paintings, drawings, prints, jewelry, books, etc.) or 1334 York Avenue (furniture, decorative arts, rugs, silver, porcelain, etc.) for the experts' inspection and advice; there is no charge for this service, but it is requested that you telephone for an appointment. Hours of inspection at 980 Madison Avenue and 1334 York Avenue are 10:00 a.m. to 5:00 p.m., Monday through Friday. If you are in doubt as to just the right place to take your property, call the appropriate department listed in the front of the catalogue.

Visits to advise clients and evaluate property can be arranged. The usual fees for such initial visits are:

Manhattan	$25.00
Other boroughs of New York City	$50.00
New York Metropolitan Area	$100.00
Elsewhere in North America	$250.00

Traveling expenses are extra and the fee is refundable in the event of consignment for sale by Sotheby Parke Bernet within one year from the date of the visit.

APPRAISALS

Appraisals may be done for insurance, estate, family division or other purposes (*excluding* gift tax).

Appraisal fees vary according to circumstances. Flat rates will be quoted based upon expert time involved, total appraised value, and costs of processing. Travel expenses are additional. Appraisals can be delivered within three weeks from the date of the appraisal visit.

A partial rebate of our fee will be made on any property subsequently consigned to us for sale within a year of our appraisal. Further information may be obtained from Miss Lauren Johnson or Mr. George Snyder, Jr., (212) 472-3452.

CURRENCY CONVERSION DISPLAY BOARD

A currency conversion display board will be operated at certain sales for the convenience of bidders. Foreign currency amounts displayed on the board are approximations determined by reference to New York foreign exchange market rates in effect at the close of business on the last business day prior to the sale. We assume no responsibility for any errors or omissions in foreign or U.S. currency amounts shown. The total purchase price and applicable taxes are payable by purchasers, in accordance with the conditions of sale, in U.S. dollars, at our offices in New York.

IMPORTANT INFORMATION FOR PROSPECTIVE BIDDERS

Please note Paragraph 8 of the Conditions of Sale dealing with the subjects of "reserves" and our "interest in offered lots other than normal selling commissions." The following definitions of terms and explanations of policies on these subjects and the implementation thereof are provided for your information and guidance.

"RESERVE"

Definition: A "Reserve" is the confidential minimum price agreed between the seller us, below which the lot will not ordinarily be sold. On unsold lots, less than full commission may be paid.

Policy: All lots marked with ■ immediately preceding the lot number are being offered subject to a reserve. Our standard advice to sellers is that reserves be set at a percentage of the mean of the estimates, generally somewhat below the low estimate shown in the estimate sheet provided with this catalogue. In no case do we permit a reserve to exceed the high estimate shown in the estimate sheet. Unsold lots, i.e., those which do not meet their reserve, are omitted from the price lists issued following sales.

Implementation: We as agent for the seller protect reserves, that is, place bids during the auction if and when the highest outstanding bid at any time during the sale is below the reserve on the lot being offered.

"OWNED PROPERTY"

Definition: "Owned property" is property which, at the time it is offered for sale at auction, is owned solely or partially by us or an affiliate (and in the sale of which we are acting as a principal and not an agent).

Policy: The purchase of property by us for sale at auction is an insignificant part of our overall business. Direct purchases are only made at the request of a client and, in these cases, only after standard commission sales or guaranteed minimum price sales have been rejected by the client. Reserve prices of property owned by us are set on the same or a lower basis than property sold for other consignors, that is, reserves usually will be set below the low pre-sale estimates provided with this catalogue and in no case will they be higher than the low estimates. Any owned property which is unsold at the auction will be omitted from the price lists following the sale. All property owned by us will be identified in the catalogue as "Property of Sotheby Parke Bernet Inc." or a similar recognizable designation. In some cases, the prior source of property will be identified, e.g., "Property from the Estate of John Doe sold by order of the present owner Sotheby Parke Bernet Inc."

Implementation: Our representatives will make no bids on our behalf except to protect a reserve placed by us as owner. Bidding by us to protect reserves on property is effected in the same way as bidding to protect reserves on property consigned by an outside seller.

"BUYER'S PREMIUM"

A premium of 10% will be added to the successful bid price of all property sold by us, whether consigned to us or "owned property" as defined above, and whether picked up or delivered, and this premium is payable by all purchasers, whether dealers, institutions, private collectors, or others.

"EXPORTATION PERMITS"

Certain property sold at auction by us may be subject to the provisions of the Endangered Species Act of 1973. In order to export these items, special licenses must be obtained from the Department of the Interior, U.S. Fish and Wildlife Service. There are no assurances that any such license can be obtained. Please contact the appropriate expert department if you have any questions.

LIST OF ARTISTS

LIST OF PRODUCTIONS

ROMANTIC BALLET
Property of Various Owners

1

WILLIAM DRUMMOND

■ 2   MADAME CELESTE as the Arab Boy in VICTOIRE!

Hand colored lithograph, London, Thos. McLean, 1838; octagonal, trimmed to the subject; a bright image aside from foxing throughout, affixed around the edges to a mount

14¾ x 11 *inches*
37.5 x 28 *cm*

Note: Victoire was a military drama first produced at the Adelphi Theatre, London on December 4, 1837

Literature

George Chaffee, "The Romantic Ballet in London", in *Dance Index*, vol. 11, nos. 9-12, 1943, no. 14, illus. p. 157
Ivor Guest, *A Gallery of Romantic Ballet, A Catalogue of the Collection of Dance Prints at the Mercury Theatre*, London, 1965, no. 43, illus.

2

■ 1   MARIE TAGLIONI (AFTER A LITHOGRAPH BY B. MULRENIN)

Watercolor and pencil   15½ x 10¾ *inches*
39.8 x 27.3 *cm*

Note: This watercolor closely resembles B. Mulrenin's lithograph of Marie Taglioni which was published in London in 1834

Literature

cf. Ivor Guest, *A Gallery of Romantic Ballet, A Catalogue of the Collection of Dance Prints at the Mercury Theatre*, London, 1965, no. 118, illus. (the lithograph)

3

ALFRED EDWARD CHALON
■ 3   THE CELEBRATED *PAS DE QUATRE:* CARLOTTA GRISI,
MARIE TAGLIONI, LUCILLE GRAHN AND FANNY CERRITO

Hand-colored lithograph, octagonal,	17½ x 15 *inches*
trimmed to the subject and laid down	44.5 x 38.1 *cm*

Note: The *Pas de Quatre,* with choreography by Jules Perrot and music by Cesare
Pugni was composed and performed by the four leading ballerinas of the Romantic
period at Her Majesty's Theatre, London, on July 12th, 1845

Literature
  Cyril W. Beaumont and Sacheverell Sitwell, *The Romantic Ballet in*
  Lithographs of the Time, 1938, no. 8, illus. p. 156
  Brian Read, *Ballet Designs and Illustration, 1581-1940,* Victoria and
  Albert Museum, 1967, no. 118, illus.

LES GLOIRES DE L'OPERA

■ 4   Two lithographs, numbers 2 and 7, from the souvenir album; partly hand colored and heightened with gum arabic; printed by Haguental, Paris, Aubert & Cie., [1846]; each plate numbered and inscribed *Gloires de l'Opéra;* depicting *Fanny Cerrito dans la Lithuanienne* and *Fanny Cerrito dans la Vivandière.* Good impressions, some foxing and staining

Image size: 10 x 8⅜ *inches*
25.3 x 21.3 *cm*
Sheet size: 15⅛ x 10¾ *inches*
38.5 x 27.3 *cm*
(2 in lot)

4

LES GLOIRES DE L'OPERA

■ 5   Two lithographs, numbers 11 and 12 from the souvenir album; partly hand colored and heightened with gum arabic, printed by Haguental and Fagonde, Paris, Aubert & Cie, [1846]; each plate numbered and inscribed *Gloires de l'Opéra;* depicting *Carlotta Grisi & Perrot, dansant La Polka,* and *Louise Fleury, dans un ballet anglais.* Good impressions, some foxing and staining

Image size: 10 x 8¾ *inches*
25.3 x 21.3 *cm*
Sheet size: 15⅛ x 10¾ *inches*
38.5 x 27.3 *cm*
(2 in lot)

5

PORTRAIT OF FANNY ELSSLER (AFTER JEAN-AUGUSTE BARRE)

■ 6 Minton Parian figure, dated October 1874, impressed MINTONS, with date cypher, a potter's mark and incised model number 162; good condition apart from some losses

Height: 13½ *inches*
34.5 cm

DANCER'S LETTERS

■ 7   CARLOTTA GRISI

Rare 3rd person ALS from Carlotta Grisi to Signor Enrico Ray

and

PIERRE GARDEL

ALS dated 1811

and

ROSITA MAURI

ALS addressing *Mon très très ami* dated January 10, 1899

(3 in lot)

6

FANNY ELSSLER

■ 8 CONTRACT between Fanny Elssler and August Belmont, dated January 7, 1843, in which Belmont is appointed Elssler's sole attorney and agent; signed by Elssler and witnessed and signed by her father Johan Elssler and by Henry Wheaton, envoy of the United States of America at the Court of His Majesty the King of Prussia

COSTUME AND DECOR DESIGNS

9

NATALIA GONTCHAROVA
■ 10 COQ D'OR

Two costume designs for a Russian peasant couple

Both signed

Pencil   Each, 16¾ x 10¼ *inches*
                                              42.6 x 26 *cm*
                                              (2 in lot)

Executed *circa* 1914

Provenance
    Grosvenor Gallery, London

Exhibitions
    London, Grosvenor Gallery, *Ballet at the Grosvenor,* 1968, nos. 7
    and 8
    Strasbourg, Ancienne Douane, *Les Ballets Russes de Serge de Diaghilev
    1909-1929,* 1969, nos. 202 and 203

10

ALEXANDRE BENOIS
■ 9 LA LOCANDIERA

Costume design for Mirandolina in the last act, framed together with
an ALS dated March 15, 1956 describing the drawing

Signed and dated 1913, titled and inscribed

Pencil and colored crayons   12⅜ x 8¾ *inches*
                                          31.4 x 22.3 *cm*

Note: Designed for a production of Carlo Goldoni's *La Locandiera* at the Moscow
Art Theater in the Spring of 1914 with Mme. Gzovskia in the role of Mirandolina

11

NATALIA GONTCHAROVA
■ 11   COQ D'OR

Design for the proscenium arch

Inscribed in Russian

Gouache   *20 x 25⅝ inches*
                                                 50.7 x 65 cm

Painted *circa* 1914

Provenance
   Ifan Kyrle Fletcher, London

NATALIA GONTCHAROVA
■ 12   LE SOIR

Costume design for *La Fiancée*

Signed; also inscribed and titled on the *verso*

Watercolor and pencil   13 x 8 *inches*
                                         33 x 20.3 *cm*

Provenance
   Acquired from the artist
   Jacques Spreiregen, Monaco

NATALIA GONTCHAROVA
■ 12A   L'OISEAU DE FEU

Costume design for the Tsar Sultan

Pencil, watercolor, silver   14⅞ x 10⅝ *inches*
and gold paint   37.8 x 27 *cm*

Note: Designed for Diaghilev's Ballets Russes revival of *L'Oiseau de Feu* which opened at the Lyceum Theater, London on November 20, 1926

12

12A

LEON BAKST
■ 13   CLEOPATRE

Costume design for a Priest

Signed, dated 1910, titled and inscribed "Le Pretre"

Pencil, watercolor and gold paint   11 x 8¼ *inches*
on laid paper   28 x 21 *cm*

CLÉOPATRE
"LE PRÊTRE"

BAKST
1910

13

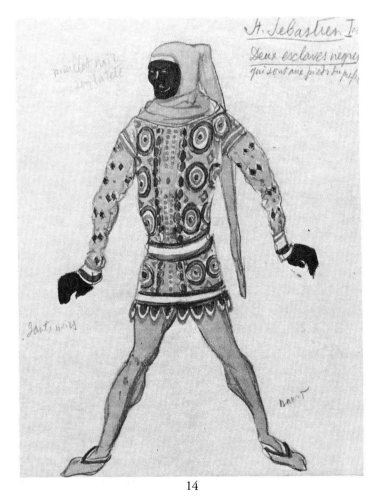

14

15

LEON BAKST

■ 14 LE MARTYRE DE SAINT SEBASTIEN

Costume Design for a Negro slave in Act I

Signed, titled and inscribed

Watercolor, pencil, gouache and silver   12¼ x 9⅜ *inches*
paint on laid paper, laid down on board   31.1 x 23.8 *cm*

   Note: *Le Martyre de Saint Sebastien* was first performed by the Ida Rubinstein
Company at the Théâtre du Châtelet, Paris on May 22, 1911 with choreography
by Fokine and decor by Bakst. The artist designed another production for Ida
Rubinstein in 1922

Provenance
   Acquired from the family of the artist

LEON BAKST

■ 15 LE MARTYRE DE SAINT SEBASTIEN

Costume design for the Emperor in Act II

Signed, titled and inscribed *1 costume très riche!* and annotated with
instructions to the dressmakers

Watercolor, pencil and gold paint   12¼ x 9⅜ *inches*
on laid paper, laid down on board   31.1 x 23.8 *cm*

   Note: See *Note* to previous lot

Provenance
   Acquired from the family of the artist

16

ALEXANDRE BENOIS

■ 16   SADKO

Design for the decor of the third tableau

Signed and inscribed; also signed, dated 1930 and inscribed *Decor de l'Opera "Sadko" III Tableau* on the *verso*

Gouache, pen and ink on laid paper   *17½ x 23½ inches*
                                                       44.5 x 59.7 cm

> *Note: Sadko* with music by Rimsky-Korsakov and decor and costumes by Benois was presented by the Compagnie de Mme Kouznetzova-Prince Zeretelli at the Théâtre des Champs-Elysées, Paris in 1930

17

ALEXANDRE BENOIS

■ 17 SADKO

Costume design for *Princess Volkhova*

Signed twice, titled and numbered 78, inscribed *Rome* and with instructions to the dressmaker; also signed and numbered 12 on the *verso*

Watercolor and pencil with traces of   11¾ x 8⅝ *inches*
gold paint on *Ingres* paper   29.8 x 22 *cm*

> *Note:* See *Note* to previous lot

ALEXANDRE BENOIS

■ 18 SADKO

Two costume designs for a Venetian and a cup-bearer

One signed with initials, the other signed; one numbered 25 the other 40; both titled and dated *Rome* 1931

Gouache and pencil on laid paper   12 x 8¾ *inches*
     30.5 x 22.2 *cm*

> *Note:* See *Note* to lot 17

18

19

LEON BAKST

■ 19 OEDIPUS AT COLONNA

Costume design for *Theseus*

Signed, titled and inscribed in Russian

Watercolor and pencil with gold   11⅛ x 8⁵/₁₆ *inches*
and silver paint   28.3 x 21.1 *cm*

> *Note:* Sophocles' play *Oedipus at Colonna,* with costumes and decor by Bakst was
> produced at the Alexandrinsky Theater, St. Petersburg in 1903

Exhibitions
> London, Grosvenor Gallery, *Ballet at the Grosvenor,* 19 November-
> 31 December, 1968, no. 2

Literature
> Charles Spencer, *Leon Bakst,* 1973, illus. p. 227

20

LEON BAKST

■ 20 DELPHI

Signed

Watercolor on paper, laid down   6⅝ x 13¾ *inches*
                                        16.8 x 34.8 *cm*

> *Note:* Bakst made a series of drawings during a trip to Greece with Serov, possibly
> in 1905, although various dates have been suggested. The sketchbook of his trip is
> now in the Dance Collection of the New York Public Library at Lincoln Center.
> Bakst's trip was the inspiration for many decors and costumes for ballets with
> Greek themes

Provenance
> Acquired from the family of the artist

Literature
> Arsène Alexandre, *Histoire de Leon Bakst,* 1924, pl. XLVIII, illus. in
> color
> Charles Spencer, *Leon Bakst,* 1973, no. 33, illus. p. 45

21

LEON BAKST

■ 21　LA BELLE AU BOIS DORMANT

Costume design for the *Fiancé Indien*

Signed and dated 1922

Watercolor, pencil, gouache and silver　26½ x 19¼ *inches*
paint on laid paper, laid down on board　67.3 x 48.8 *cm*

Provenance
　Acquired from the family of the artist

Literature
　Leon Bakst, *Inedited Works of Leon Bakst,* 1927, illus. in color p. 128

UMBERTO BRUNELLESCHI

■ 22　Costume design for *Schéhérazade*

Signed

Pen and ink, watercolor,　13 x 9¾ *inches*
gouache and gold paint　33 x 24.8 *cm*

　Note: A pencil sketch with inscription appears on the *verso*

Executed *circa* 1920

Provenance
　Lucien Goldschmidt, New York

22

23

LEON BAKST

■ 23   Design for the *Commoedia dell'Arte*

Signed, dated 1906 and inscribed in Russian *To my dear Alyosha Mavrine as a remembrance*

India ink, gouache and watercolor   8⅝ x 27⅞ *inches*
on illustration board   22 x 70.8 *cm*

> *Note:* Alexei (Alyosha) Mavrine was Diaghilev's friend and secretary during the early years of the Ballets Russes

NATALIA GONTCHAROVA

■ 24   Study for a Russian Costume

Stamped with the Russian monogram

Pencil on laid paper   12¾ x 8½ *inches*
                                                  32.4 x 21.7 cm

Note: A pencil study for a program cover dated 1935 appears on the *verso*

Exhibitions

London, Annely Juda Fine Art; Cologne, Galerie Bargera; Basel,
Galerie Liatowitsch; Milan, Galleria Milano, *Theatre, An exhibition
of 20th century theatrical designs and drawings,* Oct. 1974 - April
1975, no. 119

MIKHAIL LARIONOV

■ 25   Design for a dancer in rehearsal clothes

Signed and dated 1926

Pencil   13 x 8⅝ *inches*
                                                     33 x 22 *cm*

Provenance
   Acquired from the artist
   Jacques Spreiregen, Monaco

25

LEON BAKST

■ 26   LES ORIENTALES

Design for the decor

Pencil, squared for transfer   5¼ x 7⅞ *inches*
                                                     13.3 x 19.7 *cm*

Note: Les Orientales, with choreography by Fokine after Petipa and decor and costumes by Bakst, was first performed at the Paris Opéra on June 25, 1910 by Diaghilev's Ballets Russes

Provenance
   From the estate of Leon Bakst, Paris

Exhibitions
   London, Fine Art Society, *Bakst,* 1974, no. 14
   London, Decor Gallery, 1979
   Edinburgh, 369 Gallery, 1979

Literature
   cf. André Levinson, *Histoire de Leon Bakst,* 1924, pl. XI (the final decor)

MSTISLAV DOBOUJINSKY

■ 27   Design for a curtain

Signed

Gouache on paper,   10 x 10¼ *inches*
laid down on board   25.3 x 26 *cm*

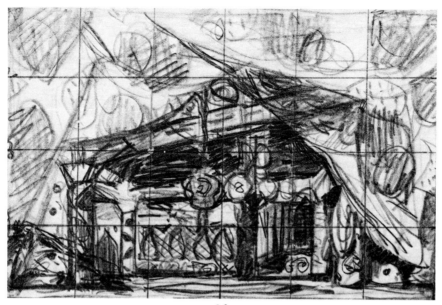

26

27

28

ALEXANDRE BENOIS
- 28 DAVID

Design for the decor

Signed with initials and dated 1928; also signed, titled "David" *de Sauguet* and dated 1928 on the *verso*

Watercolor and pencil   10¾ x 14¾ *inches*
                                                          27.3 x 37.5 *cm*

> *Note: David* was a Massine ballet with music by Henri Sauguet first performed by
> the company of Ida Rubinstein at the Paris Opéra December 4, 1928

Provenance
   Acquired from the family of the artist

29

ALEXANDRE BENOIS

■ 29 DAVID

Two Costume designs for David and a Princess

Both signed with initials and dated 1928; the one titled *David* and numbered 1e; the other inscribed *Les jeunes princesses, d'après Sandro,* numbered 10 and annotated with instructions to the dressmaker

Watercolor, India ink and pencil   12½ x 9½ *inches*
on laid paper   *31.8 x 24 cm*

Note: See *Note* to previous lot

30

ALEXANDRE BENOIS

■ 30 DAVID

Costume design for Saul

Signed and dated 1928, titled and numbered 2

Pencil, watercolor, India ink, red chalk
and gold paint on laid paper   12¾ x 8⅜ *inches*
                                                          31.2 x 23.9 cm

Note: See *Note* to lot 28

29

NIJINSKY, KARSAVINA, PAVLOVA

ROBERTO MONTENEGRO

■ 31   Three portraits of NIJINSKY in *Les Sylphides, Dieu Bleu and Jeux,* after the watercolors, numbers 1, 6 and 9 from a portfolio of his most famous roles, published by Cyril W. Beaumont in 1914; printed in gold and black; numbers 1 and 9 in good condition, number 6 slightly foxed and worn

Sheet size: 15³/₁₆ x 11¼ *inches*
38.5 x 28.6 *cm*
(3 in lot)

31A

31

A. BERT

■ 31A   NIJINSKY in LE FESTIN, silver print, 8⅝ x 5¾ *inches* (22 x 14.8 *cm*), signed by Nijinsky and dated *Paris,* 1909 on the image, with the photographer's signature blindstamped on the mount

Note: Nijinsky and Karsavina danced the Blue Bird *pas de deux* from the Sleeping Beauty as part of the divertissement *Le Festin* during the first season of Diaghilev's Ballets Russes at the Théâtre de Châtelet, Paris which opened on May 19, 1909

Literature
    Lincoln Kirstein, *Nijinsky Dancing,* 1979, illus. p. 169 (credited to L. Roosen)

ERNST OPPLER

■ 32   TAMARA KARSAVINA in SPECTRE DE LA ROSE

Drypoint, signed in pencil and numbered 10-30, on laid paper with
wide margins, in good condition

Sheet size: 19 x 14¾ *inches*
48.3 x 37.5 *cm*

32

33

E.O. HOPPE & A. BERT

■ 33   TAMARA KARSAVINA in L'OISEAU DE FEU

Silverprint, mounted, 7⅛ x 6 *inches* (18.2 x 15.2 *cm*); signed by
Karsavina on the mount

Note: One of a series of photographs by E.O. Hoppé & Bert published in a portfolio
Studies from the Russian Ballet, London, The Fine Art Society [n.d.]

34

ALPHONSE MUCHA
■ 35   BALLETS RUSSES DE DIAGHILEV

Lithographic poster printed in red with lettering in green, printed by Robaudy, Cannes, 1922, based on a maquette from 1897 and used to advertise Diaghilev's Ballets Russes season at the Théâtre de Monte Carlo, 17 April - 7 May, 1922, 48 x 33½ inches (122 x 85 cm)

Literature

cf. Paris, Grand Palais, *Mucha, 1860-1939, Peintures, Illustrations, Affiches, Arts Décoratifs,* February 5-April 28, 1980, no. A29, illus. p. 112 (another advertisement using the same image)

JEAN COCTEAU
■ 34   TAMARA KARSAVINA in SPECTRE DE LA ROSE

Lithographic poster printed in colors, signed in the stone, executed to advertise the exhibition *Ballets Russes de Diaghilev 1909 à 1929,* Musée des Arts Décoratifs, Paris, 1939, 61 x 34¾ *inches* (155 x 88.3 *cm*)

Note: Cocteau had designed two posters to advertise the first production of *Spectre de la Rose* in 1911 and the same motif was used for the 1939 exhibition

35

36

TROY KINNEY
■ 36 SPECTRE DE LA ROSE

Etching, signed in pencil, on laid paper with wide margins; good condition apart from mat stain

Sheet size: 14⅝ x 16⅝ *inches*
37.5 x 42.3 cm
Image size: 9 x 11¼ *inches*
22.9 x 28.6 cm

PER KROHG
■ 37 JEAN BÖRLIN

Lithographic poster printed in colors, signed in the stone and dated 1920, published by Publicité WALL, Paris, to advertise Rolf de Maré's Ballets Suedois; 63 x 47⅜ *inches* (160 x 121.5 *cm*)

Literature
    cf. Walter Terry and Jack Rennert, *100 Years of Dance Posters*, 1975, no. 53, illus. (a smaller version *circa* 1922)

37

38

PIERRE MOURGUE
■ 38   JEAN BÖRLIN

Lithographic poster printed in colors, signed in the stone, printed by
H. Chachoin, Imp., Paris; 63 x 47 *inches* (160 x 121.5 *cm*)

ERNST OPPLER
■ 39   ANNA PAVLOVA in THE DYING SWAN

Signed with initials

Pastel on watermarked grey paper   11¼ x 8 *inches*
                                                 28.6 x 20.3 *cm*

Note: The Dying Swan, a Fokine ballet to music by Saint-Saëns and costumes by
Léon Bakst was first performed at the Hall of Noblemen, St. Petersburg in 1905

39

ERNST OPPLER
■ 40 ANNA PAVLOVA in THE DYING SWAN

Drypoint and roulette engraving, signed in pencil and numbered III (from a limited edition of IV), on *Van Gelder* paper, with full margins, discolored down one side, otherwise in good condition

Sheet size: 20 x 13¼ *inches*
50.7 x 33.7 *cm*
Image size: 13¹¹/₁₆ x 11 *inches*
34.7 x 28 *cm*

and

ERNST OPPLER

ANNA PAVLOVA in PAPILLON

Drypoint, and roulette engraving, signed in pencil and numbered 4-30, on laid paper with full margins, in good condition

Sheet size: 15 x 10½ *inches*
38.1 x 26.7 *cm*
Image size: 9¼ x 7 *inches*
23.5 x 17.8 *cm*
(2 in lot)

41

ANNA PAVLOVA
■ 41 Silverprint of Pavlova in *Bacchanale,* 8 x 6 *inches* (20.3 x 15.3 *cm),* together with an ALS in English stating that Mr. Wladimir Worontzoff is a member of Pavlova's company, dated March 27, 1920, on Hotel Vendôme stationery *and* a letter signed V. Dandré also referring to Wladimir Worontzoff on Pavlova's personal stationery (3 in lot)

40

ANNA PAVLOVA

■ 42 A SCRAPBOOK COLLECTION, containing 11 photographs (including one portrait of Pavlova, 3 portraits of Laurent Novikoff; 6 photographs of Pavlova and various partners and one photograph of Pavlova's company in *Don Quixote*); 4 illustrated souvenir programmes; one benefit programme autographed by V. Dandré, I. Clustine and many others; 23 other programmes; one postcard of Pavlova and one of her Christmas cards; one autograph letter from Max Rabinoff regarding Pavlova's first American tour (dated New York, November 30, 1910) and 11 clippings from newspapers and magazines

JEAN COCTEAU
■ 43 ANNA PAVLOVA as THE SWAN

Lithographic poster printed in colors, signed in the stone and dated 1955, executed to advertise the exhibition *Anna Pavlova et La Danse de son Temps,* Paris, Bibliothèque-Musée de l'Opéra, January-March, 1956, 29¼ x 19⅞ *inches* (74.3 x 50.5 *cm*)

MALVINA HOFFMAN
■ 44 ANNA PAVLOVA

Rare group of 14 studio photographs by MALVINA HOFFMAN of Pavlova posing partly nude for the *Bacchanale Frieze,* [c. 1915]; comprising 6 photographs of Pavlova, 7 of Pavlova and Volinine and 1 of Volinine alone; each 5¼ x 3⅛ *inches* (13.3 x 8 *cm*); in an album; ©*Copyright retained by Malvina Hoffman Properties*

Note: Malvina Hoffman was a close personal friend of Pavlova's for many years and worked on the *Bacchanale Frieze,* a life-size bas-relief comprising 26 panels, from 1914 to 1924

43

45

ALEXANDRE BENOIS
■ 45   LA DAME AUX CAMELIAS

Design for the decor of Act I

Signed and titled; also signed, titled, numbered 25, dated 1923 and inscribed *Acte Ier (Un salon chez Marguerite Gautier/Replique de la maquette qui se trouve a la Bibliothèque de Vienne-Autriche)*

Watercolor and pen and ink   16⅞ x 24⅜ *inches*
with gouache on laid paper   42.8 x 61.8 *cm*

> *Note:* Designed for Ida Rubinstein's production of *La Dame aux Camélias* at the Théâtre Sarah Bernhardt, Paris in 1923

ALEXANDRE BENOIS
■ 46 LE BOURGEOIS GENTILHOMME

Two costume designs for a Harlequin and the Bourgeois Gentilhomme

One signed, the other signed with the initials; both dated 1932; the one inscribed *Arlequin turc pas de trois* and with instructions to the dressmaker

Watercolor, pencil and India ink on laid paper

12½ x 9½ *inches*
30.8 x 24 *cm*
(2 in lot)

Note: Le Bourgeois Gentilhomme, with choreography by Balanchine, music by Richard Strauss, libretto by Boris Kochno and decor and costumes by Benois was first performed by the Ballet Russe de Monte Carlo at the Théâtre de Monte Carlo on March 3, 1932

46

47

ALEXANDRE BENOIS
■ 47 LE BOURGEOIS GENTILHOMME

Two designs for a male and female costume

Both signed with the initials; one dated 1932 and inscribed; and with instructions to the dressmaker, the other titled and inscribed

Watercolor, gouache, pencil and India ink and gold paint on laid paper

One, 12½ x 9¼ *inches*
31.8 x 23.5 *cm*
The other, 12¼ x 9½ *inches*
31.2 x 24.2 *cm*
(2 in lot)

Note: See *Note* to previous lot. A pencil sketch of a dancer appears on the *verso* of the female costume design

48

49

50

GEORGES LEPAPE

■ 48   L'OISEAU BLEU

Design for the decor in the 2nd act, 3rd scene

Signed, titled *L'Oiseau Bleu: Le Pays du Souvenir,* dedicated *à Madame Henri de Réginîere hommage admiratif* and dated 1924

Gouache, pencil and silver paint on illustration board

10⅝ x 9⅛ *inches*
27 x 23.2 *cm*

Provenance
    Acquired from the estate of the artist

Literature
    cf. Georges Lepape, *Décors et Costumes pour L'Oiseau Bleu de Maurice Maeterlinck,* 1924, illus. p. 43

GEORGE BARBIER

■ 49   Costume design for a Lady in a lavender dress

Signed

Watercolor and ink with metallic paint

10¼ x 9¼ *inches*
26 x 23.5 *cm*

GEORGE BARBIER

■ 50   Costume design for a Lady in lavender dress

Signed

Watercolor, ink and pencil

10¼ x 9 *inches*
26 x 22.8 *cm*

50A

VALENTINE HUGO
- 50A Costume design for three masked figures

Pen and ink and watercolor

9½ x 12 *inches*
24.3 x 30.5 *cm*

51

SERGEI SOUDEIKINE
- 51 PAGANINI

Costume design for *Two Florentine Maids*

Signed and inscribed in Russian with dancer's names and with instructions to the dressmaker; also inscribed on the *verso*

Pen and ink and watercolor

11⅝ x 19⅛ *inches*
29.6 x 48.6 *cm*

Note: Fokine's ballet *Paganini* with music by Rachmaninov and scenery and costumes by Soudeikine was first produced by De Basil's Ballet Russe at Covent Garden, London on June 30, 1939

Exhibitions
London, Grosvenor Gallery, *Ballet at the Grosvenor,* 19 November-31 December, 1968, no. 43

NATALIA GONTCHAROVA
- 52 L'IMPERATRICE

Costume design

Signed, titled and inscribed *2eme* and with instructions to the dressmaker; also titled and inscribed *2eme costume des 3* on the *verso*

Watercolor and pencil
on artist's board

18⅜ x 12⅛ *inches*
46.7 x 31 *cm*

Provnenance
Jacques Spreiregen, Monaco

53

52

NATALIA GONTCHAROVA
■ 53   L'ECHARPE DE COLOMBINE

Decor design for Act II

Signed; also inscribed *2eme acte* and bears title and various inscriptions on the *verso*

Pencil and watercolor on   19⁵/₁₆ x 24¾ *inches*
on heavy paper   49.1 x 62.9 *cm*

> *Note:* Gontcharova designed the decor and costumes for *L'Echarpe de Colombine,* a pantomime-ballet by Hugo von Hofmannstahl directed by Tchebotarev and Vermel at the Kikimora Theater, Berlin in 1922

Exhibitions
> London, Grosvenor Gallery, *Ballet at the Grosvenor,* 19 November-31 December 1967, no. 14
> London, Annely Juda; Basel, Galerie Liatowitsch; Cologne, Galerie Bargera, *Theatre,* October - December, 1974, no. 14

Literature
> Mary Chamot, *Gontcharova,* 1972, illus. p. 146

54

55

NATALIA GONTCHAROVA
■ 54   MAITRE DE DANSE

Costume design

Signed, numbered *I* and annotated with instructions to the dress-maker; also titled in Russian and inscribed *Opera de Monsigny, "On ne s'avise jamais de tout"* and *Entreprise de M.N. Kouznetzouva* on the *verso*

Pencil and watercolor   *18 x 12 inches*
on artist's board   *45.8 x 30.5 cm*

Provenance
   Acquired from the artist
   Jacques Spreiregen, Monaco

NATALIA GONTCHAROVA
■ 55   L'ECHARPE DE COLOMBINE

Decor design for the final act

Signed; also bears title and inscription *Dernier acte* on the *verso*

Pencil, watercolor and gold   *19 x 27³/₁₆ inches*
paint on heavy paper   *48.3 x 69.1 cm*

   Note: See *Note* to lot 53

Exhibitions
   London, Grosvenor Gallery, *Ballet at the Grosvenor,* 19 November-
   31 December 1968, no. 13, illus.
   London, Annely Juda; Basel, Galerie Liatowitsch, Cologne, Galerie
   Bargera, *Theatre,* October - December 1974, no. 123

LEON BAKST

■ 56   LA BELLE AU BOIS DORMANT

Costume design for *L'Oiseau Bleu*

Signed, dated 1921, titled and inscribed *M. Idsikowsky 5 acte* and with instructions to the dressmaker

Pencil and watercolor with gold and silver paint on laid paper, laid down

13 x 9½ *inches*
33.3 x 24.2 *cm*

56

ROBERT EDMOND JONES

The Property of the Dartington Hall Trust

57

ROBERT EDMOND JONES
■ 57   TILL EULENSPIEGEL

Design for the decor

Black crayon, India ink and grattage and grey wash on paper, laid down

7½ x 10 *inches*
9 x 25.4 *cm*

Note: Till Eulenspiegel was the last ballet choreographed by Nijinsky. With music by Richard Strauss and decor and costumes by Robert Edmond Jones, it was first produced by Diaghilev's Ballets Russes at the Manhattan Opera House, New York, on October 23, 1916. Robert Edmond Jones had worked with Max Reinhardt and was the only American artist chosen by Diaghilev to design a Ballets Russes production. "In the ballet *Till Eulenspiegel,* the artistic approach of Old Russia and the artistic approach of new America met and fused for the first time" (v.i. Robert Edmond Jones p. 45)

Provenance
Miss Dorothy Whitney, New York
The Dartington Hall Trust (bequeathed by the above)

Literature
Robert Edmond Jones, *Drawings for the Theatre,* 1925, illus. pl. 3
Robert Edmond Jones, "Nijinsky and Till Eulenspiegel" in *Dance Index,* New York, vol. IV, no. 4, April 1945, pp. 44-56
Cyril Beaumont, *Ballet Design Past and Present,* 1946, illus. p. 82
Walter René Fuerst and Samuel J. Hume, *Twentieth-Century Stage Decoration,* 1967, illus. pl. 242

58

The Property of the Dartington Hall Trust

ROBERT EDMOND JONES
■ 58   ROMEO AND JULIET

Design for the decor in Act I, Scene 1, *A Public Place*

Pencil and colored crayons   16⁵/₁₆ x 19¼ *inches*
on grey paper   41.4 x 48.9 *cm*

> *Note:* Designed for an Arthur Hopkins production of *Romeo and Juliet* which opened
> at the Longacre Theater, New York, on December 27, 1922 with Ethel Barrymore

Provenance
  Miss Dorothy Whitney, New York
  The Dartington Hall Trust (bequeathed by the above)

59

ROBERT EDMOND JONES

■ 59 MACBETH

Decor design for the meeting with the Three Witches

Black crayon and grattage   11 x 14½ *inches*
on paper, laid down   28 x 36.9 *cm*

Note: Designed for Hopkins' production of *Macbeth* at the Apollo Theater, New York, February 17, 1921 with Lionel Barrymore in the title role. The production was described as follows: "There was a stage enclosed with a background of black, flat so that no light was caught to break the complete darkness of it . . . Three great tragic masks were hung to the front, high above the action, and from them vast daggers of light poured down, crossed, pierced, flooded the action below, as in the witches' scene or the banquet" (v.i. *The Theatre of Robert Edmond Jones*, p. 5)

Provenance
    Miss Dorothy Whitney, New York
    The Dartington Hall Trust (bequeathed by the above)

Literature
    Robert Edmond Jones, *Drawings for the Theatre*, 1925, illus. pl. 12
    Ralph Pendleton, ed., *The Theatre of Robert Edmond Jones*, 1958 (reprinted 1977), p. 5

60

ROBERT EDMOND JONES
■ 60 HAMLET

Design for a back curtain

Pen and India ink, black   11 x 14 *inches*
crayon and grattage on paper   28 x 35.6 *cm*

> *Note:* Designed for an Arthur Hopkins production of *Hamlet* which opened at the
> Sam H. Harris Theater, New York, on November 16, 1922 with John Barrymore
> in the title role

Provenance
  Miss Dorothy Whitney, New York
  The Dartington Hall Trust (bequeathed by the above)

Literature
  Robert Edmond Jones, *Drawings for the Theatre,* 1925, illus. pl. 21

61

ROBERT EDMOND JONES
■ 61   HAMLET

Decor design for a court scene

Pen and India ink, black crayon and grattage on paper

11⅜ x 13¼ *inches*
28.9 x 33.7 *cm*

Note: See *Note* to previous lot

Provenance
Miss Dorothy Whitney, New York
The Dartington Hall Trust (bequeathed by the above)

Literature
Robert Edmond Jones, *Drawings for the Theatre,* 1925, illus. pl. 20

ROBERT EDMOND JONES
■ 62   THE ANCIENT MARINER

Design for the decor

Pencil, pen and India ink and wash on paper, laid down

10½ x 12½ *inches*
26.6 x 31.7 *cm*

Note: Designed for Eugene O'Neill's dramatization of S.T. Coleridge's poem *The Ancient Mariner* which opened at the Provincetown Playhouse on April 16, 1924. Jones also co-directed the production with James Light

Provenance
Miss Dorothy Whitney, New York
The Dartington Hall Trust (bequeathed by the above)

Literature
Robert Edmond Jones, *Drawings for the Theatre,* 1925, illus. pl. 33

62

MUSIC HALL AND CABARET

Property of Various Owners

MSTISLAV DOBOUJINSKY
■ 63   LES COSAQUES DE PLATOFF A PARIS

Signed and dated 1926 and with inscription *The Cossacks in Paris 1815 Chauve Souris;* also bears inscription *Les Cosques* (sic) *de Platoff a Paris en 1815 Maquette de M. M. Doboujinsky* on the *verso*

Ink and watercolor with	12 x 9 *inches*
gouache on laid paper	30.5 x 22.9 *cm*

64

NIKOLAI BENOIS
■ 64   LA GRANDA OPERA ITALIANA

Decor design for the *Théâtre de la Chauve-Souris*

Signed, dated 1925 and inscribed

India ink and pencil with traces of watercolor on laid paper
9½ x 12⅝ *inches*
24.3 x 32 *cm*

Note: Nikita Balieff opened the Théâtre de la Chauve-Souris in 1908 in Moscow where he presented operas, operettas, drama, comedy and ballet. In 1920 Balieff left Moscow and took his theater to Paris, London and the United States

Literature
cf. *Théâtre de la Chauve-Souris de Nikita Balieff, Saison 1924-25,* souvenir program, p. 12 (illus. of a painted version of this design)

and

NIKOLAI BENOIS

Design for clocks

Signed, dated 1921 and inscribed *Pour Balieff*

Pencil on laid paper
9½ x 12½ *inches*
24.2 x 31.2 *cm*
(2 in lot)

63

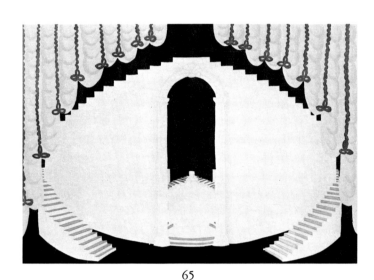

65

PAUL RANSON
■ 66   FOLIES-BERGÈRE

Costume design for *Les Citrons*

Signed; also bears inscriptions and a sketch on the *verso*

Gouache and pencil   20 x 12⅞ *inches*
                                            50.8 x 32.7 *cm*

and

PAUL RANSON

FOLIES-BERGÈRE

Costume design for *La Cible*

Signed and inscribed   17¾ x 12⅞ *inches*
Pencil, gouache and silver paint   45.1 x 32.7 *cm*
                                            (2 in lot)

FOLIES-BERGÈRE
■ 65   (i) Decor Design

Pencil, gouache, collage   14¼ x 20¼ *inches*
and gold paint   36.2 x 51.5 *cm*

(ii) Curtain Design

Signed ENDRÉ

Gouache and gold paint   12¾ x 17⅞ *inches*
                                     32.4 x 45.3 *cm*

(iii) Decor design

Pencil, gouache and silver paint   12⅜ x 16 *inches*
                                     31.5 x 40.6 *cm*
                                          (3 in lot)

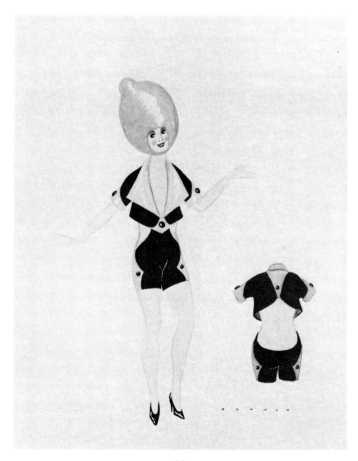

66

and

ALEC SHANKS

L'OMBRE DE LA MODE

Two costume designs

Both signed and one dated 30

India ink, watercolor
and silver paint

Each, 18⅜ x 14¾ *inches*
46.7 x 37.6 *cm*
(3 in lot)

67

ALEC SHANKS
■ 67   L'OMBRE DE LA MODE

Decor design

Signed, titled and inscribed with lighting instructions

India ink, watercolor
and silver paint

11¼ x 15¼ *inches*
28.7 x 38.7 *cm*

67

ERTE

■ 68   LES FANTÔMES

Decor for the *Bal Tabarin*

Signed; also inscribed *N 7882*, titled and stamped *Composition Originale ERTE, ROMAIN DE TIRTOFF* on the *verso*

Gouache on paper

Sheet size: 14⅞ x 10⅞ *inches*
37.8 x 27.8 cm
Image size: 5½ x 6⅝ *inches*
14 x 17 cm

Note: Between 1933 and 1952 Erté designed costumes and sets for Pierre Sandrini's revues at the Bal Tabarin theater in Paris

69

68

ERTE

■ 69   L'EXPOSITION DE 1900

Le Cake Walk

Costume design for one of 8 dancers

Signed; also titled, numbered 12.469 and inscribed on the *verso*

Gouache

14½ x 10¾ *inches*
36.8 x 27.3 cm

ERTE

■ 70   Costume design for a South American production at the Latin Quarter, New York

Signed; also stamped *Composition originale ERTE ROMAIN DE TIRTOFF* on the *verso*

Gouache

14½ x 10¾ *inches*
36.8 x 27.3 cm

Executed in 1961

Exhibitions

Boston, Boston Center for the Arts, *Costumes of the Latin Quarter*, November 15, 1978-January 15, 1979, illus. in color

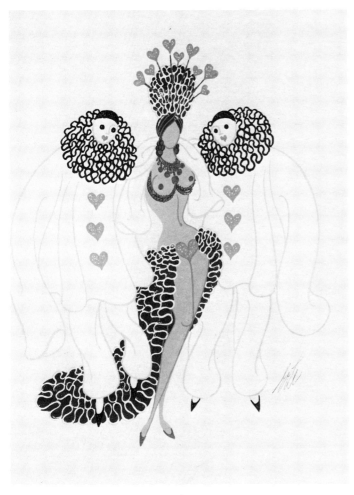

70

MARCEL VERTES
■ 71 BLUEBEARD

Costume design

Signed and stamped with the atelier mark, *recto* and *verso*

Watercolor and pencil on   14 x 11 *inches*
illustration board   35.6 x 28 *cm*

Note: Mikhail Fokine's *Bluebeard* with music by Offenbach and decor and costumes by Vertès was first produced by Ballet Theater at the Palacio de Bellas Artes, Mexico City on October 27, 1941

and

MARCEL VERTES

KATINKA

Costume design for *La Marquise*

Signed

Gouache and pencil on   13¾ x 10¼ *inches*
illustration board   35 x 26.1 *cm*

Note: Katinka by Paul Nivois and Lesthay was presented at the Théâtre de l'Empire, Paris in 1932. A sketch of a sailor inscribed *Vieux Loup de Mer* appears on the *verso*

and

MARCEL VERTES

TRANSATLANTIC RHYTHMS

Design for the decor *and* costume design: a double-sided drawing

Signed on the *verso* and stamped with the atelier stamp, *recto* and *verso*

Gouache and silver paint on   9¼ x 12 *inches*
illustration board   23.5 x 30.1 *cm*
                                            (3 in lot)

71

72

PAUL COLIN
■ 72 *L'HOMME ET LA MACHINE* AU CASINO DE PARIS

Design for the decor

Titled, dated 1930, numbered 83 and stamped with the *vente* stamp on the backing

Gouache and charcoal on paper,   18¼ x 23 *inches*
laid down on board   46.3 x 58.4 *cm*

   Note: The ballet *L'Homme et la machine* was performed at the Casino de Paris in 1934

Provenance
   Vente Paul Colin, Paris, 1970

Literature
   cf. Cyril W. Beaumont, *Ballet Design, Past & Present,* 1946, p. 134
   (illus. of another version of the decor)

73

JOSEPH URBAN
■ 73   ZIEGFELD FOLLIES

Stage design for a library scene

Signed, inscribed *Follies* and dated 1919

Watercolor, pen and ink on   11¼ x 10 *inches*
illustration board   28.6 x 25.5 *cm*

74

ANTHONY NELLÉ

Anthony Nellé, a premier danseur with the Imperial Russian Grand Opera in Warsaw
came to the United States with Pavlova's company as a lead character dancer in 1921.
He worked with Sol Hurok and the Roxy and Fox theaters in the 1920's and '30's as a
designer of revues, operas and movies. During the 1930's he also staged revues in
London and Berlin. The following designs will be included in a forthcoming book on
Nellé to be published by *Rizzoli International Publications Inc.* Spring 1981

ANTHONY NELLÉ
■ 74   LA GIOCONDA

Stage design

Stamped with the artist's stamp, *recto* and *verso;* numbered 59M and
titled *La Gioconda - Ballet III Parody - Night*

Gouache, India ink and pencil   15¾ x 20 *inches*
                                          40 x 50.8 *cm*

Note: Designed for a production at the Fox Theater, Detroit in 1928

ANTHONY NELLÉ
■ 75   DANCING NOTES

Stage design

Stamped with the artist's stamp on the *verso;* titled and numbered 62R

Gouache and India ink, silver paint and collage with moveable cut-out
to show set change

                                          15½ x 20 *inches*
                                          39.4 x 50.8 *cm*

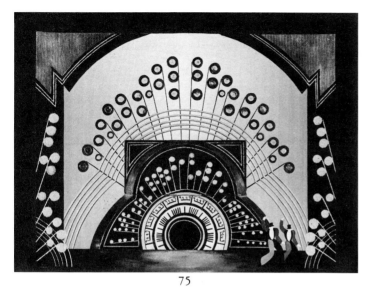

75

75

76

77

ANTHONY NELLÉ
■ 76 ROULETTE AT MONTE CARLO - NO. 2

Stage design

Stamped with the artist's stamp on the *verso;* titled, numbered 24R and 19 and inscribed *Full Stage Set*

| Gouache and India ink with | 15½ x 20 *inches* |
| gold paint and collage | 39.4 x 50.8 *cm* |

Note: Roulette at Monte Carlo *was part of a revue entitled* Folies en Parade *presented at the Prince of Wales Theater, London, in December 1934. Two diagrams of the stage plan appear on the* verso

ANTHONY NELLÉ
■ 77 TRANSATLANTIC - NO. 1

Stage design

Stamped with the artist's stamp on the *verso;* titled and numbered 73M

| Gouache and collage | 15½ x 20 *inches* |
| | 39.4 x 50.8 *cm* |

78

79

MARCEL VERTES
■ 78   TRANSATLANTIC RHYTHMS

Decor design

Signed and stamped with the Atelier mark, *recto* and *verso*

Gouache on illustration board   10⅛ x 13¾ *inches*
                                              25.7 x 35 *cm*

> *Note:* Vertès designed the decor and costumes for *Transatlantic Rhythms* at the
> Adelphi Theatre, London in 1936

and

MARCEL VERTES

Costume design for Spanish dancers

Signed in pencil and stamped with the Atelier mark

Gouache and pencil with traces of gold paint on illustration board
                                              13¾ x 10¼ *inches*
                                              35 x 26.1 *cm*
                                              (2 in lot)

Executed *circa* 1932

Provenance
   Dora Vertès

MARCEL VERTES
■ 79   Two costume designs for a male and female figure

Signed

Watercolor and pencil; one on artist's board, the other on paper laid
down on board

                              One, 17 x 11⅜ *inches*
                                    43.2 x 29 *cm*
                      The other, 15 x 10⅞ *inches*
                                    38.1 x 27.7 *cm*
                                    (2 in lot)

> *Note:* On the *verso* of the male costume there is a sketch of two dancers

GEORGES DE POGEDAIEFF

■ 80   Costume design for three figures *and* costume design for three satyrs

Both signed and dated 36 and numbered on the *verso*

Watercolor and charcoal heightened with white on *Ingres* paper, the second laid down on board

The first: 18 x 22 *inches*
45.7 x 55.9 *cm*
The second: 21⅜ x 17¾ *inches*
55.2 x 45.2 *cm*
(2 in lot)

80

81

SERGEI SOUDEIKINE
■ 81   DECOR DESIGN

Signed; also bears inscription *"Chinese Temple"* Radio City Music Hall on the *verso*

Gouache and India ink with faint traces of gold paint

7¼ x 11⅝ *inches*
18.5 x 29.6 *cm*

Note: Soudeikine designed several productions for Radio City Music Hall between 1936 and 1939

CECIL BEATON
■ 82   FOLLOW THE SUN

Design for a woman's costume in *The First Shoot*

Signed

Watercolor on board   18½ x 13⅞ *inches*
                                        47 x 35.2 *cm*

Note: The First Shoot, a ballet with story by Osbert Sitwell for a C.B. Cochran
Revue *Follow the Sun* was produced in 1936

Provenance
  James Forrestal, Washington, D.C.

Literature
  cf. Charles Spencer, *Cecil Beaton, Stage and Film Design,* 1975, p. 35
  (illus. of the decor)

82

SERGEI SOUDEIKINE
■ 83   THEATRICAL DESIGN

Signed

Gouache, watercolor and India   17 x 11⅝ *inches*
ink on paper, laid down   43.2 x 29.5 *cm*

ALEXANDRA EXTER
■ 84   STAGE DESIGN

Signed and dedicated *A Grace Frisby* on the mount

Gouache and collage   7 x 8⅝ *inches*
                                        17.8 x 21.9 *cm*

Provenance
  Estate of Grace Frisby, New York

PAVEL TCHELITCHEW
■ 85   SAVONAROLA

Costume designs for a "Hellenist" and for a Lady

One signed, titled, inscribed *Berlin* and with annotations and numbered 34; the other signed, titled, numbered 18, inscribed and dated
1921 *Berlin*

One gouache on paper laid down on board;
The other gouache and pencil on paper   20 x 14⁵/₁₆ *inches*
laid down on board   50.8 x 36.3 *cm*
                                        (2 in lot)

Note: Savonarola, a tragedy after the Comte de Gobineau's book *The Renaissance,*
was designed by the artist for the Koeniggratzerstrasse Theater in Berlin *circa*
1921-22

Provenance
  Jane Heap, Paris

83

84

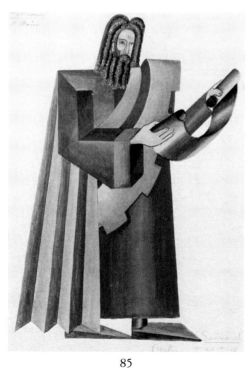

85

85

OSKAR SCHLEMMER
■ 86 DAS NUSCH-NUSCHI

Decor design for the final scene

Inscribed *Das Nusch-Nuschi, (letzter Bild)* and *(Blei-Hindemith)* by the artist on the mount; also stamped *Oskar Schlemmer/Bauhaus Weimar* on the mount

Watercolor, pencil, gold
and silver paint on paper

Image size: 6⅝ x 10¾ *inches*
17 x 27 *cm*
Mount size: 12¾ x 16⅛ *inches*
32.5 x 41 *cm*

Note: Das Nusch-Nuschi, a one-act play inspired by Burmese puppets by Franz Blei with music by Paul Hindemith was first produced at the Württembergischen Landestheater, Stuttgart on June 4, 1921. Schlemmer designed the sets and costumes for this and other productions while head of the Bauhaus workshop for wall decoration. The theme of man as puppet was central to his work for the theater and to his essentially humanistic art in general. Ernst Scheyer sums up Schlemmer's views as follows: "The irrevocable process of mechanization, which threatens to change man into a robot and woman into a doll can be alleviated by fantasy, humor and irony. This then is the meaning of the puppet's mechanically repeated affirmation: 'No puppet-just an art figure.' " (*v.i.* Scheyer p. 37)

Executed in 1921

Literature

Ernst Scheyer, "The Shapes of Space: The Art of Mary Wigman and Oskar Schlemmer" in *Dance Perspectives,* 41, Spring 1970, pp. 29-48
cf. Karin V. Maur, *Oskar Schlemmer Oeuvrekatalog,* 1979, no's. A79-491, illus. p. 225-227 (13 other designs for *Das Nusch-Nuschi*)

86

87

ALEXANDRA EXTER
■ 87   LES EQUIVOQUES D'AMOUR

Costume design

Signed; also bears inscription on the *verso*

Gouache and pencil on   22⁹/₁₆ x 17⁷/₁₆ *inches*
paper, laid down   57.3 x 44.4 *cm*

> *Note:* Designed for a play by Francis de Miomandre

Executed *circa* 1933

Provenance
   Acquired from the artist
   Simon Lissim, New York

Exhibitions
   New York, The New York Public Library, *Artist of the Theatre,*
   Alexandra Exter, Spring-Summer 1974, no. 72, illus. p. 35

KURT SELIGMANN
■ 88   THE GOLDEN FLEECE

Costume design for *Saturn*

Signed and inscribed *Kipp;* also inscribed *Kipp; auf der ellbogen* on the
verso

Gouache and India ink   14¾ x 11¾ *inches*
on grey paper   37.5 x 30 *cm*

> *Note:* Designed for the first production of Hanya Holm's *The Golden Fleece (An Alchemist Fantasy),* a ballet based on the elements and the planets which opened on March 17, 1941 at the Mansfield Theater, with Kipp Kiernan in the role of Saturn. A design for an armband appears on the *verso*

Provenance
   M. Knoedler and Co., New York

Literature
   cf. *Hanya Holm Collection,* New York Public Library for the Performing Arts, Folder XIV, no. 403 (photograph of Kipp Kiernan as *Saturn*).

88

89

EUGENE BERMAN
■ 89   DEVIL'S HOLIDAY (LE DIABLE S'AMUSE)

Signed, titled, inscribed *Taverne* and dated 1939

Watercolor and India ink	8 x 11 *inches*
with gouache	20.2 x 28 *cm*

Note: The Devil's Holiday, with choreography by Frederick Ashton and decor by
Eugene Berman was first produced October 26, 1939 by the Ballet Russe de
Monte Carlo at the Metropolitan Opera House in New York

NATALIA GONTCHAROVA
■ 90   Decor design

Inscribed *for Lifar* on the *verso*

Watercolor and pencil	21¼ x 28¼ *inches*
on heavy paper	54 x 71.8 *cm*

90

LEON BAKST
■ 91 LE MARTYRE DE SAINT SEBASTIEN

Design for the decor of Act V, *Paradis Transformé*

Signed, dated 1922, titled and inscribed with instructions to the scene
designers

Watercolor, gouache and   17⅝ x 12 *inches*
pencil on laid paper   44.8 x 30.5 *cm*

> *Note:* See *Note* to lot 14
> This work was executed with some assistance from the atelier

ALEXANDRE BENOIS
■ 92 RAYMONDA

Design for the decor in Act II

Signed, titled, dated xii. 1945 and inscribed; also inscribed on the *verso*

Pencil, pen and ink   9¾ x 13 *inches*
and watercolor   25 x 33 *cm*

> *Note:* Benois designed the decor and costumes for a production of *Raymonda* in New
> York in 1945

91

92

ALEXANDRE BENOIS

■ 92A AN IMPORTANT SCRAPBOOK COLLECTION, comprising 24 drawings by Benois in pencil and pen, most dated and inscribed, including: 2 designs for 17th century costumes annotated with instructions to the pattern maker, several drawings showing medieval dress, a view of an interior of a theater showing the orchestra and decor, 15 travel views of European towns and historic sites, 12 theater and opera programs annotated with Benois' notes on the performances, 5 small hand-written notes and a variety of other material including 2 letters to Benois signed by Rolf de Maré and Pierre Tugal and a photograph of a 17th century decor in Benois' collection *autographed Coll. Alexandre Benois*

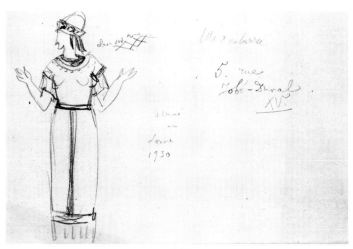

92A

ALEXANDRE BENOIS

■ 93 PETROUCHKA

Costume design for a woman in the crowd

Signed twice, numbered 58, inscribed *Jeune Dame Amie de la Comtesse* and with instructions to the dressmaker; also signed and inscribed *Petrouchka Une Dame* on the *verso*

Pencil, India ink and	12⅜ x 9⅛ *inches*
watercolor on paper	31.5 x 23.2 *cm*

94

ALEXANDRE BENOIS

■ 94 LE LAC DES CYGNES

Two costume designs for *La Danse Polonnaise*

Both signed, titled, dated 1945 and inscribed with instructions to the dressmaker; one numbered 21, the other 22

India ink and watercolor with traces of gold paint on laid paper, laid down

Each: 10⅞ x 8¼ *inches*
27.3 x 21 *cm*
(2 in lot)

93

ALEXANDRE BENOIS
■ 96   LE LAC DES CYGNES

Costume design for Prince Siegfried in the First and Second Act *and*
Costume design for a Lady in Court dress in the Third Act

Both signed and titled, one dated 1945, both numbered and inscribed
with instructions to the dressmaker

India ink and watercolor with traces
of gold paint on *Ingres* paper

The first: 10¾ x 7⅞ *inches*
27.3 x 19.8 *cm*
The second: 9¾ x 6¼ *inches*
24.8 x 15.9 *cm*
(2 in lot)

Note: Executed for a production of *Swan Lake* commissioned by Sol Hurok, New
York in 1945

96

95

NATALIA GONTCHAROVA
■ 95   DECOR DESIGN

Bears title *Isles Act I* and various other inscriptions on the *verso*

Watercolor and pencil on paper

19¼ x 25⅛ *inches*
48.9 x 63.8 *cm*

ALEXANDRE BENOIS
■ 97 LE ROI NU

Three costume designs for figures in the crowd

Signed with initials, titled, inscribed and two dated 1940

India ink and watercolor on   9½ x 6⅛ *inches*
Ingres paper   24.1 x 15.5 *cm*
                                                         (3 in lot)

> *Note:* Benois designed the decor and costumes for the Paris production of the ballet *Le Roi Nu* in 1940

98

97

NATALIA GONTCHAROVA
■ 98 DECOR DESIGN

Bears title *Isles Variation* and various other inscriptions on the *verso;* also authenticated by M. Larionov on the *verso*

Watercolor and pencil on paper   19⅝ x 25½ *inches*
                                                 49.8 x 64.8 *cm*

ENRICO CARUSO

■ 100   PORTRAIT OF MARCEL JOURNET as MEPHISTO *and* CARICATURE, POSSIBLY OF GATTI-CASAZZA: A PAIR OF DRAWINGS

One signed and dated 1911

Pencil

The first: 5¾ x 3¾ *inches*
14.7 x 9.5 cm
The second: 5½ x 5 *inches*
14 x 12.7 cm
(2 in lot)

NIKOLAI BENOIS

■ 101   TSAR SALTAN

Design for the curtain

Signed and dated 27 and inscribed in Russian on the mount: *Curtain for Rimsky-Korsakov's opera Tsar Saltan designed by Nikolai Benois staged by A.A. Sanin for the La Scala production 1928 season*

Gouache and pencil with gold and silver paint,
squared for transfer and affixed along the upper edges to a mount
9 x 13½ *inches*
22.8 x 34.3 cm

Note: Rimsky-Korsakov's opera *Tsar Saltan* with text by Belsky after a poem by Pushkin was first produced in Moscow on November 3, 1900

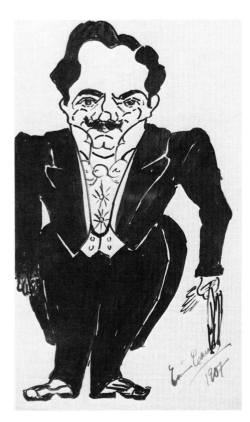

99

ENRICO CARUSO

■ 99   SELF-PORTRAIT

Signed and dated 1907

India ink and pencil

14 x 8½ *inches*
35.6 x 21.7 cm

NATALIA GONTCHAROVA

■ 102   SADKO

Costume design for a Red-spotted fish

Signed with the Russian monogram and numbered 6

Gouache and pencil with foil
collage, laid down on board
8½ x 7 *inches*
21.5 x 17.8 cm
Board side: 10⅛ x 7½ *inches*
5.8 x 19 cm

Note: Gontcharova designed the decor and costumes for the revival of *Sadko* during the Ballets Russes first American tour, which opened in New York at the Manhattan Opera House on October 16, 1916.
A detail of a decor design inscribed with dancer's names appears on the *verso* of the board

101

102

VLADIMIR IVANOVICH JEDRINSKY
■ 103 PRINCE IGOR

Design for the decor

Signed and dated 54; also titled, dated Zagreb-London 1955 and
inscribed *Rideau de scène* on the mount

Gouache and ink with	10⅝ x 11⅛ *inches*
traces of gold paint	27 x 29.5 *cm*

and

VLADIMIR IVANOVICH JEDRINSKY

PRINCE IGOR

Design for the decor

Inscribed in Russian on the *verso*

Gouache and ink with	12⅜ x 17¼ *inches*
traces of gold paint	31.4 x 43.8 *cm*
	(2 in lot)

104

103

SERGEI SOUDEIKINE
■ 104 THE MAGIC FLUTE (DIE ZAUBERFLÖTE)

Two costume designs

Both signed and inscribed in Russian; one numbered 24 the other 26

India ink and water color with gold and silver paint, laid down
Each, 14⅛ x 8⅞ *inches*
36.2 x 22.7 *cm*
(2 in lot)

Note: Soudeikine designed the decor and costumes for the Metropolitan Opera's
production of Mozart's *The Magic Flute* which opened in New York on November
6, 1926

105

ALEXANDRE BENOIS
■ 105   RIGOLETTO

Costume design for *Maddalena*

Signed with initials, titled and dated XI 1951

Watercolor, ink and pencil   *9¾ x 6½ inches*
                                              24.7 x 16.4 cm

Provenance
  The family of the artist

VLADIMIR IVANOVICH JEDRINSKY
■ 106   KHOVANSHCHINA

Four costume designs

Two signed with the initials and dated 59, all authenticated by the artist's widow in Russian, one inscribed *Khovanshchina,* the others variously inscribed

Pencil, watercolor and   Average size: *14½ x 10½ inches*
traces of gold and silver   *37 x 26.7 cm*
                                                      (4 in lot)

Note: Designed for a production of Mussorgsky's opera at the Nice Opera House in 1961

106

106

107

108

BORIS ANISFELD

■ 107 Costume design for an Oriental dancing girl, possibly in AZIADE, 1926

Signed and inscribed

Gouache and gold paint on illustration board	14 x 10 *inches* 35.5 x 25.4 *cm*

VLADIMIR IVANOVICH JEDRINSKY,

■ 108 PRINCE IGOR

Costume design for Igor

Titled and titled in Russian, inscribed *Opéra de Nice* and *Der Khan;* also authenticated by the artist's widow in Russian on the *verso*

Pencil, watercolor and gold paint	14¾ x 10½ *inches* 37.3 x 26.7 *cm*

Note: Designed for a production at the Opéra de Nice in 1959

and

VLADIMIR IVANOVICH JEDRINSKY

Costume design

Titled *Marouf,* also titled, dated 1963 and authenticated by the artist's widow in Russian

Pencil, watercolor and gold paint	14¾ x 10½ *inches* 37.3 x 26.7 *cm* (2 in lot)

NICHOLAS ROERICH
■ 109 SNEGOUROTCHKA

Scene and costume design

Signed with the monogram

Gouache on paper, laid down	15⁷/₁₆ x 15⁹/₁₆ *inches* 39.2 x 39.5 *cm*

Note: Rimsky-Korsakov's opera *Snegourotchka (The Snow Maiden)* was first performed in St. Petersburg in 1880-1882 and was first staged by the Chicago Civic Opera with sets and costumes by Nicholas Roerich in 1922

Exhibitions
New York, Cordier and Ekstrom, *Nicholas Roerich, Decors and Costumes for Diaghilev's Ballets Russes and Russian Operas,* November-December 1974, illus.

109

SERGEI SOUDEIKINE

■ 110 LE ROSSIGNOL (THE NIGHTINGALE)

Design for the decor of Act I

Signed; also inscribed *1st Act/ "The Nightingale" by Stravinsky/ Metropolitan Opera Season 1925-26-* on the backing

Watercolor and colored crayons with
pencil and gouache on paper,   *16½ x 25⅜ inches*
laid down on board   *40.8 x 64.5 cm*

> *Note:* Soudeikine designed the Metropolitan Opera's production of Stravinsky's *Le Rossignol* which opened in New York on March 6, 1926

110

111

112

EUGENE BERMAN
■ 111 IL BARBIERE DI SIVIGLIA (THE BARBER OF SEVILLE)

Design for the decor in Act II

Signed with the initials, titled and dated 1953

India ink, watercolor and colored   9¾ x 12¾ *inches*
crayons on paper, laid down   24.8 x 32.4 *cm*

> *Note:* Eugene Berman designed the decor and costumes for the Metropolitan Opera's production of Rossini's *Il Barbiere di Siviglia* which opened in New York on February 19, 1954

EUGENE BERMAN
■ 112 DECOR DESIGN

Signed with the initials, titled *Projet de décoration murale* and dated 1938

Pen and India ink and watercolor on   7½ x 11 *inches*
laid paper, affixed to a mount   19.1 x 21 *cm*

NORMAN BEL GEDDES
■ 113 AIDA

Stage design for Act IV

Signed and titled

Watercolor, India ink and pencil   21¾ x 24¼ *inches*
on artist's board   54.3 x 61.6 *cm*

> *Note:* Designed for a production during the 1933-34 season at the Metropolitan Opera House, New York

ANTONI CLAVE
■ 114 CARMEN

Design for the decor

Signed; inscribed on the *verso* of the mount *Revanche 3me tableau*

Gouache on paper,   15 x 20 *inches*
laid down on board   38 x 51 *cm*

> *Note: Carmen,* a ballet choreographed by Roland Petit, with Bizet's music, was first produced by the Ballets de Paris de Roland Petit at the Prince's Theater, London, February 21, 1949 with Zizi Jeanmaire as Carmen and Roland Petit as José

Provenance
  Galerie J. Le Chapelin, Paris
  Matthew Brown, New York

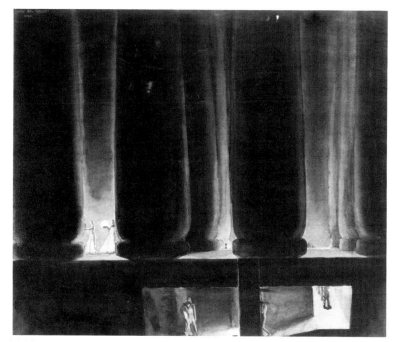

113

114

115

ALEXANDRE BENOIS
■ 115 CARMEN

Costume design for a male dancer in the 4th act

Signed, titled, numbered 35 and dated 1931, inscribed *d'après l'autori ttrato de Fokine* and with instructions to the dressmaker

Pen and ink and watercolor on laid paper	12¼ x 9¼ *inches* 31.2 x 23.6 *cm*

and

ALEXANDRE BENOIS

LA FAVORITA

Costume design for a young girl

Signed and dated 1945, titled and inscribed *4 Jeunes Filles à la Cour*

Pen and India ink and watercolor on laid paper	9½ x 6¼ *inches* 24.2 x 16 *cm*
	(2 in lot)

ALEXANDRE BENOIS
■ 116 ANDREA CHENIER

Design for the decor of Act I

Signed and dated 3 I 49; also signed and titled on the *verso*

Watercolor and pencil with ink and gouache	12¾ x 19¾ *inches* 32.3 x 50.2 *cm*

Note: Benois designed the decor and costumes for the 1951 production of Giordano's Andrea Chenier at La Scala, Milan

Provenance
   Acquired from the family of the artist

116

**Property from the Estate of
Thomas Schippers, New York**

EUGENE BERMAN
■ 117 AMAHL AND THE NIGHT VISITORS

Design for the decor

Signed with the initials, titled and dated 52 and dedicated on the mount *To Tommy (Amahl) Shippers* [*sic*] *with very sincere appreciation and friendship*

Gouache, watercolor and ink	7⅞ x 10⅞ *inches* 20 x 27.7 *cm*

Note: Amahl and the Night Visitors by Gian-Carlo Menotti, the first opera written for television, was produced by NBC on December 24, 1951 and staged at Indiana University on February 21, 1952

117

Property of Various Owners

KURT SELIGMANN
■ 118   THE UNICORN, THE GORGON AND THE MANTI-CORE

Costume design for a male dancer in the 4th act

Signed with initials, titled and dated '58

Colored crayons and pencil on page from spiral pad, partially laid down on board

11⅞ x 8¾ *inches*
30.3 x 22.4 *cm*

Note: Gian-Carlo Menotti's *The Unicorn, The Gorgon and the Manticore,* a madrigal for 10 dancers, was produced by the Walker Art Center, Minneapolis, Department of Performing Arts on June 6 and 7, 1958. Seligmann was commissioned to do a series of designs for the ballet in conjunction with an exhibition of his paintings and drawings

118

119

MSTISLAV DOBOUJINSKY
■ 119   GUERRE ET PAIX (WAR AND PEACE)

Designs for costumes

Signed with the monogram

Gouache and pencil on paper	6⅝ x 9½ *inches*
laid down on board	16.9 x 24.1 *cm*

Note: Doboujinsky designed the costumes and sets for Prokofiev's *War and Peace,* a project to be staged by G. Graf and Emil Cooper at the Metropolitan Opera, New York in 1947

CECIL BEATON
■ 120   ADRIANA LECOUVREUR

Two costume designs for an Amazon and a Dancing Boy

Both signed, titled and inscribed Act III

Watercolor and gouache on	The one: 19¾ x 13 *inches*
grey paper	50.2 x 33.1 *cm*
	The other: 19¾ x 12½ *inches*
	50.2 x 30.8 *cm*
	(2 in lot)

Note: There is a sketch of a man's head on the *verso* of the Dancing Boy. Designed for a production of Cilèa's *Adriana Lecouvreur* at the Metropolitan Opera, New York

120

121

SERGEI SOUDEIKINE
■ 121   PORGY AND BESS

Signed

Oil on canvas   16 x 28 *inches*
                                                  40.8 x 71.1 *cm*

Note: Porgy and Bess, with music by George Gershwin, lyrics by Du Bosc Heyward
and sets by Soudeikine was first performed by the Theater Guild in Boston at the
Colonial Theater on September 30, 1935

122

ANDRE DERAIN
■ 122   MAM'ZELLE ANGOT

Design for the decor

Stamped with the atelier mark (Lugt no. 668a)

Gouache on heavy *Arches* paper   19½ x 25⅞ *inches*
                                                    49.5 x 65.8 *cm*

Note: Derain designed the decor for the Sadler's Wells production of Massine's
Mam'zelle Angot, a ballet in three scenes with music by Charles Lecocq which
opened at Covent Garden, London on November 26, 1947

Exhibitions

London, Annely Juda Fine Art; Cologne, Galerie Bargera; Basel,
Galerie Liatowitsch; Milan, Galleria Milano; *Theatre, An exhibition
of 20th century theatrical designs and drawings,* October 1974-April
1975, no. 90, illus.

GEORGES YAKOULOFF

■ 122A   Costume design

Pencil, watercolor and silver paint   10½ x 7 *inches*
                                                       26.7 x 17.8 *cm*

122B

122A

GEORGES YAKOULOFF

■ 122B   Costume design

Inscribed

Pencil, India ink and watercolor   10½ x 7 *inches*
with traces of gold and silver paint   26.8 x 17.8 *cm*

123

FERNAND LEGER
■ 123   DAVID TRIOMPHANT

Decor design for the Throne Room

Watercolor and pencil on   8⅝ x 11½ *inches*
heavy paper   22 x 29.3 *cm*

> *Note:* Serge Lifar's ballet *David Triomphant* with music by Debussy and Mussorgsky
> and decor and costumes by Léger was first performed at the Théâtre de la Maison
> Internationale des Etudiants, Paris, on December 15, 1936. The ballet was
> performed at the Paris Opéra in May 1937

Provenance
   Jean Badovici, Paris

ALEXANDRA EXTER
■ 123A   ROMEO AND JULIET

Costume design

Gouache   23¼ x 15¾ *inches*
                                                  59 x 40 *cm*

> *Note:* Exter designed the costumes and decor for a production of *Romeo and Juliet*
> adapted by Shershenievich which opened at the Kamerny Theatre, Moscow on
> May 17, 1921

123A

AN IMPORTANT GROUP OF DESIGNS BY CHAGALL FOR *ALEKO*

Aleko, a ballet in one act and four scenes, with choreography by Massine to Tchaikovsky's Trio in A Minor was first produced by Ballet Theater (now American Ballet Theater) at the Palacio de Bellas Artes, Mexico City on September 8, 1942. The New York premiere at the Metropolitan Opera House took place on October 2, 1942.

Marc Chagall arrived in New York from Paris in the summer of 1941. Soon thereafter Lucia Chase, director of Ballet Theater asked him to collaborate with Léonide Massine on the production of a ballet based on a narrative folk poem by Alexander Pushkin entitled "Les Bohémiens".

The collaboration of the two Russian emigrés on the project was intense; for several months during the spring of 1942 they worked together on the ballet usually at Chagall's apartment. Chagall involved himself in the choreography and some of his sketches for the ballet contain indications of the stage action.

In August 1942 the two men went to Mexico to prepare for the opening of the ballet. Chagall himself painted the backdrops for the set and supervised every detail of the stage property and costumes. Contemporary accounts and the evidence of these designs show his close involvement in the production. Every ribbon and dancing shoe had to follow his specifications. Several sketches are inscribed with dancers' names and he was careful to write his instructions to the dressmaker in both Spanish and French.

This set of designs for costumes, headdresses and shoes, all executed on thin paper, remained in the possession of the wardrobe mistress of the Palacio de Bellas Artes for many years and has never been seen outside Mexico. A major portion of Chagall's designs for *Aleko* are in the Museum of Modern Art, New York, and it has been possible to identify most of the subjects in this group from the full-figure designs in the museum

MARC CHAGALL
■ 124 ALEKO

Three costume designs for a Gypsy (seen from the rear) in Scene I, a Woman with White Scarf in Scene III and a Peasant in Scene III

The first numbered 12, the second numbered 29 and the third numbered 28

Pencil and watercolor

The first, 5 x 4⅜ *inches*
12.7 x 11.2 *cm*
The second, 5⅝ x 5 *inches*
14.3 x 12.7 *cm*
The third, 3¾ x 5⅞ *inches*
8.7 x 15 *cm*
(3 in lot)

Note: Full-length designs for all of these costumes are in the collection of the Museum of Modern Art, New York (nos 137.45.13, 137.45.22 and 137.45.27)

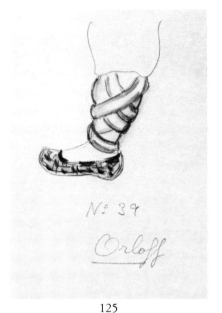

125

124

125

MARC CHAGALL
■ 125 ALEKO

Three designs for dancer's shoes

The first inscribed *Zapatos de baile blancos ocultos por la falda, Souliers blancs de danse caches par la jupe* and numbered 46, the second numbered 39, the third numbered 11; all inscribed with dancers' names

Watercolor and pencil

Each, 8¾ x 6 *inches*
22.2 x 15.2 *cm*
(3 in lot)

124

MARC CHAGALL
■ 126 ALEKO

Three designs for a Gypsy and a Society Lady in Scene IV and a Street Dancer in Scene II

The first numbered 11, the second numbered 63 and the third numbered 22

Pencil and watercolor

The first, 4⅜ x 4½ *inches*
10.7 x 11.4 *cm*
The second, 6⅛ x 5⅜ *inches*
15.6 x 13.3 *cm*
The third, 5¼ x 3¾ *inches*
13.4 x 8.7 *cm*
(3 in lot)

Note: Full-length studies of the Gypsy (in a group of four), the Society Lady and the Street Dancer (in a group of the Street Dancer and Gypsy) are in the collection of Museum of Modern Art, New York (nos. 137.45.51, 137.45.31 and 137.45.16)

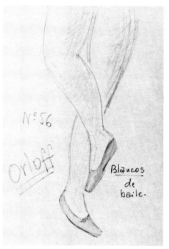

127

126

127

MARC CHAGALL
■ 127 ALEKO

Four designs for dancer's shoes

The first inscribed *Blancos de baile* and numbered 56, the second inscribed *Zapatos blancos de baile, souliers blancs de danse* and numbered 25, the third numbered 8 and the fourth numbered 2,3a,1a,1,3; all inscribed with dancers' names

Pencil and watercolor (the second pencil only)

Each: 8¾ x 6 *inches*
22.2 x 15.2 *cm*
(4 in lot)

128

MARC CHAGALL
■ 128 ALEKO

Four costume designs for a Fortune Teller in Scene II, a Man with Wine-bottle (2 views) and a Russian Baba in Scene IV

The first numbered 19, the second and third numbered 33 and the fourth numbered 49

Pencil and watercolor

The first, 5¾ x 5⅞ *inches*
14.7 x 15 *cm*
The second and third, 3 x 5¼ *inches*
7.6 x 13.6 *cm*
The fourth, 5⅝ x 4⅝ *inches*
11.2 x 11.2 *cm*
(4 in lot)

Note: Full-length studies of the Fortune Teller (shown with a Gypsy) and the Russian Baba (shown with a cow) are in the collection of the Museum of Modern Art, New York (nos. 137.45.10 and 137.45.47)

128

MARC CHAGALL
■ 129 ALEKO

Costume design for a Duke in military costume in Scene IV; design for a Hat and design for a Gypsy Lover

The first inscribed *medaille argent, medalla plateada* and numbered 48, the second inscribed *chapeau pour porter seulement dans la main, sombrero para llevarlo solamente en la mano* and numbered 48, the third numbered 6

Pencil and watercolor

The first, 3⅞ x 5⅛ *inches*
10 x 13 *cm*
The second, 5¼ x 4⅛ *inches*
13.3 x 10.3 *cm*
The third, 3⅝ x 6⅛ *inches*
9.3 x 15.5 *cm*
(3 in lot)

Note: Full-length studies of a Duke similar to the one sold here and of the Gypsy Lover are in the collection of the Museum of Modern Art, New York (nos. 137.45.33 and 137.45.8)

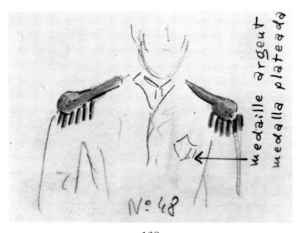

129

129

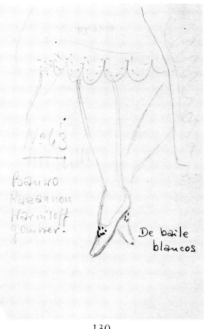

130

130

MARC CHAGALL

■ 130   ALEKO

Two designs for a Horse in Scene II and a Rooster in Scene IV *and* Three designs for dancers' shoes

The first inscribed *Nillo* and numbered 20; the second inscribed *Popora* and numbered 57; the shoes all numbered and inscribed

Watercolor and pencil   Each: 8¾ x 6 *inches*
                                        22.2 x 15.1 *cm*
                                        (5 in lot)

Note: Chagall's designs for the full figure of the horse and the rooster are in the collection of the Museum of Modern Art, New York (nos. 137.45.11 and 137.45.41)

JULIO CASTELLANOS
■ 131 MARUJILLA

Two costume designs for a children's play

One inscribed *Marujilla* and *El mismo traje en azul para Laura,* the other signed on the *verso* and inscribed *Rosquitin y Lunarcito;* both inscribed with names of performers on the *verso*

Gouache and pencil   Both: 13⅜ x 9 *inches*
                                            34 x 28.8 *cm*
                                            (2 in lot)

Provenance
   Acquired from the artist
   Josefina Piñeiro, Mexico City

Literature
   Siete, "La Costurera de Bellas Artes", December 7, 1973, p. 50, illus. in color (the female costume)

132

131

AUGUSTIN LAZO
■ 132 Two designs for eighteenth century costumes

Both signed, one inscribed *Hero: Sr. Moreau en rojo* and the other *Conde: Sr. Massé en marfil Sr. Nicolas en azul*

Watercolor, pencil and chalk   Both: 9½ x 6⅝ *inches*
on wove paper   24.1 x 16.8 *cm*
                                      (2 in lot)

Provenance
   Acquired from the artist
   Josefina Piñeiro, Mexico City

Literature
   Siete, "La Costurera de Bellas Artes" December 7, 1973, p. 50, illus. in color (one of the pair)

133

JOSE REYES-MEZA
■ 133 BALADA MAGICA

Two costume designs, one for *Warrior Spirits* and the other for the *God of War*

Both signed, titled, inscribed with dancer's names and dedicated to Josefina Piñeiro

Gouache and pencil   Both: 10 x 7½ *inches*
                                                         25.2 x 19 *cm*

and

JOSE REYES-MEZA

Design for a female costume

Inscribed with instructions to the dressmaker and with names of dancers

Gouache and pencil   12 x 9¾ *inches*
                                                         30.4 x 24.7 *cm*
                                                         (3 in lot)

Provenance
   Acquired from the artist
   Josefina Piñeiro, Mexico City

LEONOR FINI
■ 134 LES DEMOISELLES DE LA NUIT

Costume design for Agatha, the White Cat and two other cats

Signed

Gouache and watercolor on olive   12⅝ x 10 *inches*
green paper, affixed to a mount   32 x 25.3 *cm*

Note: Les Demoiselles de la Nuit, a one-act ballet with story by Jean Anouilh, choreography by Roland Petit and decor by Leonor Fini was first produced at the Théâtre Marigny, Paris on May 22, 1948 with Margot Fonteyn in the role of Agatha, the White Cat

Literature
   Jean Anouilh, *Les Demoiselles de La Nuit, Argument de Ballet,* in: *Vogue,* Paris, June 1948, illus. in color p. 66

134

135

ERTE

■ 135   BALLET ERIK SATIE

Design for the decor

Signed; also titled, numbered 18309 and inscribed *2e aspect du decor* and *1er version* on the backing

Gouache with gold paint   8¼ x 13⅜ *inches*
                                           21 x 34 *cm*

Note: Roland Petit commissioned Erté to design the costumes and decor for a ballet based on Erik Satie's music. The ballet was never produced

Executed in 1976

Exhibitions
    Coral Gables, Florida, The Lowe Art Museum, The University of Miami, *Erté on Stage,* September 5-30, 1979

LEONOR FINI

■ 136   LES BONNES

Two costume designs

One signed, the other signed and titled

India ink and watercolor on two   17⁶/₁₆ x 13⅜ *inches*
pages from a sketchbook   44 x 34 *cm*
                                           (2 in lot)

Note: Jean Genet's play *Les Bonnes,* directed by Jean Marie Serreau and with decor and costumes by Fini was presented by Jean Louis Barrault and Madeleine Renaud at the Odéon Théâtre de France in 1961

Exhibitions
    London, Annely Juda Fine Art; Cologne, Galerie Bargera, Basel, Galerie Liatowitsch, Milan, Galleria Milano, *Theatre, An exhibition of 20th century theatrical designs and drawings,* Oct. 1974 - April 1975, no. 105 (one exhibited)

136

137

NATALIA GONTCHAROVA

■ 137   Costume design for a dancing girl

Signed with initials; also inscribed in Russian on the *verso*

Watercolor, pencil and gold paint   14¾ x 8½ *inches*
                                               37.3 x 21.6 *cm*

136

138

Property from the Estate of Mrs. Benjamin Sonnenberg

PAVEL TCHELITCHEW

■ 138   The Dressing Room

Signed and dated 32

Brown ink and wash   10½ x 8¼ *inches*
                                             26.8 x 21 *cm*

139

Property of Various Owners

LEONOR FINI

■ 139   LE CONCILE D'AMOUR

Two costume designs for the Dame de Borgia, one inscribed *Dona Sancia*

Signed and inscribed

India ink and gold paint; one with
fabric swatch attached, on two   One: 15¾ x 13⅜ *inches*
pages from a sketchbook   40 x 34 *cm*
                                                    The other: 16¼ x 13 *inches*
                                                            41.3 x 33.2 *cm*
                                                                (2 in lot)

Note: Panizza's *Le Concile d'Amour* with costumes by Leonor Fini and decor by Jorge
Lavelle was produced at the Théâtre de Paris in 1968

Exhibitions
    London, Annely Juda Fine Art, Cologne, Galerie Bargera, Basel,
    Galerie Liatowitsch, Milan, Galleria Milano, *Theatre, An exhibition
    of 20th century theatrical designs and drawings,* Oct. 1974 - April
    1975, no. 103 (one exhibited)

LEONOR FINI

■ 140   LE CONCILE D'AMOUR

Costume for the *Deuxieme Courtisane*

Signed, titled and inscribed

Pen and ink, gold paint and watercolor with sequins and fabric
swatches, on a page from a sketchbook

                                                    14½ x 12⅛ *inches*
                                                        36.7 x 31 *cm*

Note: See *Note* to lot 139

140

FILM

141

SALVADOR DALI
■ 141   DESTINO

Design for the film

Signed

India ink and pencil on a
page from a notebook

Image size: 6 x 8 *inches*
15.2 x 20 *cm*
Sheet size: 8 x 9 *inches*
20.3 x 22.9 *cm*

Note: In 1947 Dali collaborated with Walt Disney on a film, *Destino*. Although
never completed, it was a blend of live action and animation dealing with the
themes of time and love and including a baseball game ballet

ED BEEMER
■ 142   FAN-FAN FOLLIES

Costume design

Signed and dated 1920

Watercolor and pencil with
traces of gold paint

16⅛ x 11½ *inches*
41.3 x 29.2 *cm*

Note: Designed for a slapstick short by Mack Sennet in the 1920's

VINCENT KORDA
■ 143   THINGS TO COME

Six etchings: Designs for the sets

Signed in pencil

Etching

Image size, approx.: 9½ x 11¾ *inches*
24.2 x 30 *cm*
Sheet size, each: 12 x 18 *inches*
30.5 x 45.7 *cm*
(6 in lot)

Note: The futuristic film, *Things to come* based on H.G. Wells' novel *The Shape of
Things to Come* was produced by London Films in 1936 with Ralph Richardson and
Raymond Massey

143

144

CHRISTIAN BERARD

■ 144 LA BELLE ET LA BÊTE

Design for the film

Signed

India ink and wash on   12⅛ x 9⅛ *inches*
paper, laid down on board   30.9 x 23.2 *cm*

Note: Bérard did the decor for Jean Cocteau's 1946 film version of Perrault's *La Belle et la Bête*

Executed *circa* 1946

CHRISTIAN BERARD

■ 144A SOUVENIR DU THEATRE DE LA MODE

Signed, titled and dated *Londres, Sept.* 45

Gouache and watercolor   12 x 10 *inches*
                                                         30.5 x 25.5 *cm*

Note: Designed for a souvenir program for the *Théâtre de la Mode,* a French fashion presentation organized by Berard, Boris Kochno, Jean Cocteau and Georges Wakevitch in 1945

144A

PORTRAITS

145

146

147

JEAN COCTEAU

■ 145   Portrait of Jean Marais

Signed and dated *Montargis 38*

Pencil   12⅛ x 9¾ *inches*
                                          30.7 x 23.8 *cm*

Provenance
  Jean Marais, Paris

MIGUEL COVARRUBIAS

■ 146   WILL ROGERS

Signed

Brush and ink on heavy   13⅜ x 9⅝ *inches*
paper, laid down   34 x 24.5 *cm*

and

DANCERS

Signed and inscribed *"and gold paint for Adaggio dancers"*

Pen and ink with   14 x 10 *inches*
watercolor on paper   35.5 x 25.5 *cm*
                                    (2 in lot)

LISA RHANA

■ 147   PORTRAIT OF RUDOLF NUREYEV

Signed; also inscribed on mount *Rhana original* and signed, titled, dated and inscribed on the backing

Pastel on paper   13½ x 10½ *inches*
affixed to a board   34 x 26.8 *cm*

Executed in 1965

148

ENZO PLAZZOTTA
■ 148   ANTHONY DOWELL IN PRACTICE CLOTHES

Stamped bronze plaques on base: One bearing the artist's name and the edition number 8/9, the other stamped with the foundry mark *FOND NB*

Bronze, brown patina;   Height (excluding base):
on black stone base   14 *inches*
                                                                    35.5 *cm*

Executed in 1972

ENZO PLAZZOTTA
■ 149   ANTHONY DOWELL AND ANTOINETTE SIBLEY REHEARSING FOR ASHTON'S *THE DREAM*

Stamped with the artist's name and numbered 9/9; also stamped with the foundry mark *Fonderia Luigi Tomassini*

Bronze, brown patina;   Height (excluding base): 14½ *inches*
on black stone base   37 *cm*

Executed in 1973

ENZO PLAZZOTTA
■ 150   ANTHONY DOWELL AND ANTOINETTE SIBLEY REHEARSING FOR ASHTON'S *THE DREAM*

Stamped with the artist's name and numbered 6.9

Brown, brown patina;   Height (excluding base): 13 *inches*
on black stone base   33 *cm*

Executed in 1972

149

150

151

EDWARD GORDON CRAIG
■ 151 THE DOME

Colored woodcut, signed in pencil; also bears inscription *Woodblock print by Gordon Craig greatly reduced for The Dome, Jan-March 1899,* with wide margins, good condition

Sheet size: 8¼ x 6⅜ *inches*
21 x 16.3 *cm*
Image size: 5 x 3¾ *inches*
12.8 x 9.5 *cm*

EDWARD GORDON CRAIG
■ 152 NANON AND PUNCHINELLA

Signed, titled and dated 1903

Pencil, ink, wash   12½ x 10¹/₁₆ *inches*
and watercolor   31.8 x 25.6 *cm*

Note: Pulchinella characters featured in Craig's designs for some years after he saw a Pierrot show at Southwold in 1897

Exhibitions

London, Decor Gallery, *Edward Gordon Craig, Claud Lovat Fraser and some Contemporaries,* June 1979, no. 22

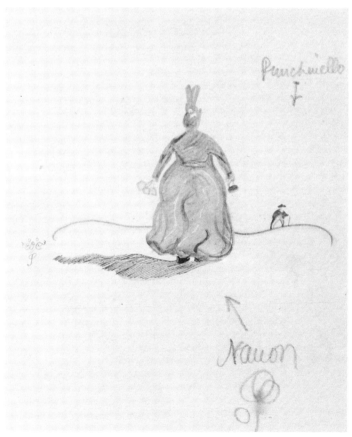

152

153

JESSIE M. KING

■ 153 A PLAY BASED ON THE ARTHURIAN ROMANCES

Twenty-nine costume designs together with a manuscript list of the costume designs in the artist's hand

All inscribed

All pencil, pen and wash   Average size: 10¼ x 8 *inches*
                                                      27 x 20 *cm*
                                                    (29 in lot)

> *Note:* The designs include costumes for *The Lady of the Lake, Anglides, Dame Liones, The Lady of Avelion, Queen Morgan le Fay, The Queen of the Outer Isles* and *The Queen of the Eastlands*

Provenance
   Merle Taylor Collection (Sale: Glasgow, Sotheby Parke Bernet & Co., *Jessie M. King and E.A. Taylor, Illustrator and Designer,* June 21, 1977, lot 198)

153

ALBERT RUTHERSTON

■ 154   Costume design for two dancing girls

India ink on thin paper   7½ x 6⅜ *inches*
                                           19 x 16.2 cm

**ELLEN TERRY, SARAH BERNHARDT, LILLIAN RUSSELL
AND ALLA NAZIMOVA**

■ 155   Autograph inscriptions, three on small cards, one on Hotel
Baltimore Stationery

"Tis safer to be that which we destroy than by destruction dwell in
doubtful joy" signed Ellen Terry, Lyceum Theatre, Feb. 1889

"Que Dieu vous benisse" signed Sarah Bernhardt, 1906

"Truly yours" signed Lillian Russell

"—but when I think of my vocation life does not seem to be so hard"
signed Alla Nazimova   (4 in lot)

156

154

Signed DOT

■ 156   DR. FAUST AND MISS MARGUERITE

THE GUARDS BURLESQUE LANCERS

Signed, dated February 1888, titled *"Dr. Faust and Miss Marguerite"*,
and inscribed *the enormously successful burlesque by R. Martin, Esq. on
tunes introduced into and arranged by E. Solomon Esq. dedicated to the
Guards Burlesque Company*

Watercolor and gouache on   12¹¹/₁₆ x 8⅞ *inches*
paper, laid down on board   *32.3 x 22.6 cm*

157

**JEAN BERAIN the Elder, JEAN BERAIN the Younger and
FOLLOWERS (Late 17th/Early 18th Century)**
■ 157 COSTUME DESIGNS FOR THE OPERA DE PARIS, 2
volumes containing 44 original watercolors, laid down, some with
inscriptions (26 in the first volume and 18 in the second), each approx.
11½ x 7½ *inches* (29.2 x 19 *cm*); with the bookplate of RUDOLPH
VALENTINO

Folio, half leather, marbled boards and marbled end papers
Some foxing, generally good condition

GEORGES LEPAPE
■ 158 L'OISEAU BLEU by MAURICE MAETERLINCK, Rare 2
volume set

(i) L'OISEAU BLEU, *Féerie, avec quatorze aquarelles originales de
Georges Lepape,* Paris, "Le Livre", 1925; with 14 colored line block
stencils by J. Saudé after the watercolors by Georges Lepape,
Number XI from a limited edition of 435 (numbers I to XXV
published *hors commerce* for collaborators: this one especially
printed for Claude Lepape, the artist's son)

(ii) DECORS ET COSTUMES POUR L'OISEAU BLEU DE
MAURICE MAETERLINCK, *Avec une préface de Gérard
D'Houville,* Paris, Société d'Edition "Le Livre", 1927; with 61
colored colotype stencils by J. Saudé after the watercolors by
Georges Lepape, *Number XI from a limited edition of 225* (this
number printed for Claude Lepape)

Small quarto
Half-blue leather and silver boards with silver lettering on spine, in
case
Very good condition, some staining opposite line block plates

A.E. JOHNSON
■ 158A THE RUSSIAN BALLET, with illustrations by René Bull;
London, Constable & Co. Ltd., 1913; with many illustrations in the
text; *dedicated for Minna with best Christmas wishes from Ola Cockcroft* and
dated 1916 on the fly leaf; together with Bull's original drawing for
Karsavina and Bolm in *Thamar*

Cover somewhat faded and rubbed;   (2 in lot)
Spine frayed at both ends
Text and plates in good condition

W. A. PROPERT

■ 159 THE RUSSIAN BALLET IN WESTERN EUROPE, 1909-1920, *with a chapter on the music by Eugène Goossens and sixty-three illustrations from original drawings;* New York, John Lane Company, 1921; signed by Stravinsky on an illustration of his portrait by Jacques-Emile Blanche, *Number 297 from a Limited Edition of 450 copies*

Quarto; original boards

Spine faded; slightly separating

ANDRE LEVINSON

■ 160 L'OEUVRE DE LEON BAKST POUR LA BELLE AU BOIS DORMANT; Paris, M. de Brunoff, 1922; with 54 plates in color and an illustration of Bakst's portrait by Picasso as a frontispiece; *Number 494 from a Limited Edition of 500*

Large quarto
Excellent condition

ARSENE ALEXANDRE

■ 161 L'ART DECORATIF DE LEON BAKST, *Notes sur les Ballets par Jean Cocteau,* Paris, Maurice de Brunoff, 1913; 77 plates, with 50 in color, illustrating the artist's designs for productions from 1909-1913. *From a limited edition of 80 luxury examples published with an original watercolor by Leon Bakst* (the watercolor offered separately as lot 13)

Large quarto, vellum binding embossed in gold, in original case
Excellent condition; case worn at edges and missing part of spine

LEON BAKST

■ 162 INEDITED WORKS OF LEON BAKST, *Essays on Bakst by Louis Réau, Denis Roche, V. Svietlov and A. Tessier,* New York, Brentano's, 1927; with 30 full-page plates, 5 in black and white or sanguine and 25 stenciled in watercolor, gold and silver, as well as illustrations and decorative borders in the text; *Number 200 from a Limited Edition of 600*

Large quarto, original decorated boards
Good condition, spine slightly separating, some staining on pages opposite illustrations and decorations in the text

ARSENE ALEXANDRE

■ 163 L'ART DECORATIF DE LEON BAKST, *Notes sur les Ballets par Jean Cocteau,* Paris, Maurice de Brunoff, 1913; 77 Plates, with 50 in color, illustrating the artist's designs for productions from 1909-1913

Large quarto, half vellum, gilt decorated
Excellent condition

ANATOL PETRIZKY

■ 164 THEATER-TRACHTEN, text by B. Chmury, Staatsverlag der Ukraine, 1929; text in German and Ukrainian; with 56 plates tipped in of which 29 are in color, illustrating Petrizky's designs for productions from 1922-1928

Large quarto, original wrappers
Plates in fine condition, wrappers worn, spine separating

164

EDWARD STARK

■ 165 CHALIAPIN, Russian edition, St. Petersburg, R. Golicke and A. Willborg, 1915; dedicated by the author and dated August 15, 1919; illustrated with 58 photographs of the artist in his most famous roles

Quarto
Boards separating
Some foxing throughout; otherwise good condition

ANDRE LEVINSON

■ 166   HISTOIRE DE LEON BAKST, Paris, Société d'Editions et de Librairie Henri Reynaud, 1924; dedicated to Gabriel Hpranderi "mon cher directeur et ami" by André Levinson and dated January 10, 1925; with 68 plates and illustrations in the text; *Number VII from a special hors commerce edition numbered I to XV*

Large quarto; bound in burgundy calf with an embossed harlequin and mask
Excellent condition

PABLO PICASSO

■ 167   LE TRICORNE, Trente-deux reproductions des maquettes en couleurs; Paris, Editions Paul Rosenberg, 1920, *Number 121 from a Limited Edition of 250*

Small quarto
Original wrapper and boards
Good condition

MARIE LAURENCIN

■ 168   LES BICHES, 2 vols., Paris, Editions des Quatres Chemins, 1924; *Number 259 from a limited edition of 335;* vol. I contains 14 illustrations by Marie Laurencin, articles by Jean Cocteau and Darius Milhaud; vol. II has a frontispiece photograph of Marie Laurencin by Man Ray and 21 photographs of the dancers

Small quarto
Good condition, some foxing on title page of vol. II, boards rubbed

GEORGES BRAQUE

■ 169   LES FACHEUX, 2 vols., Paris, Editions des Quatres Chemins, 1924; *Number XL from a special hors commerce edition of 75 copies;* vol. I contains an article and portrait of Georges Auric by Jean Cocteau, an article by Louis Laloy; a piano score by Georges Auric and 23 color plates by Georges Braque; vol. II has a frontispiece photograph of George Braque by Man Ray and 22 photographs of the dancers

Small quarto, original paper wrappers, in publisher's case
Books in good condition; case worn and torn

ANDRE DUNOYER DE SEGONZAC

■ 170   VINGT-QUATRE DESSINS SUR SCHEHERAZADE; Paris, François Bernouard, 1910

Original paper wrapper
Good condition, wrapper worn

Note: The first book illustrated by Dunoyer de Segonzac

and

THEATRE DE CHATELET GRANDE SAISON DE PARIS: Souvenir program, Paris, May-June 1912; cover illustration after Bakst showing costume design for Ida Rubinstein in the role of Hélène; photographic illustrations after Bakst and photographs of the performers within gold decorative borders   (2 in lot)

171

EDWARD GORDON CRAIG

■ 171   HENRY IRVING. ELLEN TERRY. A BOOK OF PORTRAITS, Chicago, R.R. Donnelly for Herbert S. Stone, 1899; with 19 color plates after Craig's designs of Ellen Terry and Henry Irving in their well-known roles; *Rare;* (created from drawings commissioned for *The Chap-Book* in 1898 which were not used when the magazine was discontinued in July, 1898)

Original boards, separating at spine, edges rubbed
Original cardboard folding case, soiled
Plates in good condition

EDWARD GORDON CRAIG

■ 172   SOUVENIR. ACIS AND GALATEA. MASQUE OF LOVE. Souvenir album of the plays as produced at the Great Queen Street Theatre, March 10th, 1902, with 17 illustrations by Craig of which 7 are in color

Small quarto, original wrappers, worn, text and plates in good condition

together with EDWARD GORDON CRAIG

NOTHING OR THE BOOKPLATE, with a handlist by E. Carrick, London, Chatto and Windus, 1925, with 26 bookplates designed by Craig

Small quarto, original boards, some foxing, otherwise good condition

and EDWARD GORDON CRAIG

ON THE ART OF THE THEATRE, London, William Heinemann, 1924, with 15 illustrations by the author

Octavo, original boards, some foxing, plates in good condition

and EDWARD GORDON CRAIG

SCENE, with a Foreword and Introductory Poem by John Masefield, London, Humphrey Milford, Oxford University Press, 1923, with 19 illustrations by Craig and 4 other illustrations

Large quarto, some foxing, plates in good condition

(4 in lot)

EDWARD GORDON CRAIG

■ 173   THE MASK. *A Journal of the Art of the Theatre;* Volume One, no. 3 & 4, May - June 1908; Volume One, no. 5, July 1908; Volume Eleven, no. 1, January 1925; Volume Fifteen, no. 1, Jan.-Feb.-March, 1929

Original wrappers; two large quarto, two small quarto; one wrapper foxed and stained, the other stained; good internally   (4 in lot)

V. SVETLOV

■ 174   LE BALLET CONTEMPORAIN, Russian edition, edited with the collaboration of Leon Bakst, St. Petersburg, R. Golicke and A. Willborg, 1911

Quarto
Cloth binding decorated in green and gold, frayed and missing spine
Text and plates in good condition

ANDRE LEVINSON

■ 175   L'OEUVRE DE LEON BAKST POUR LA BELLE AU BOIS DORMANT, Paris, 1922, M. de Brunoff, *Number 290 from a Limited Edition of 500*

Large quarto, original paper wrappers, in case
Good condition
and

ARSENE ALEXANDRE

L'ART DECORATIF DE LEON BAKST, *Notes sur les Ballets par Jean Cocteau,* Paris, 1913, Maurice de Brunoff, 77 plates, with 50 in color

Large quarto, half vellum, gilt decorated
Good condition   (2 in lot)

■ 176   TEN RUSSIAN BOOKS on the ballet: (1) Mikhail Fokine, *Against the Flow, Memoirs of a Ballet Master,* Moscow, 1962; (2) Bogdanov-Berezovskii, *Ulanova,* Moscow, 1961; (3) Albert Kahn, *Days with Ulanova,* Moscow, 1963; (4) N. Stukolkina, *Quatre Exercises,* Moscow, 1972; (5) Bogdanov-Berezovskii, *Articles on the Ballet,* Leningrad, 1962; (6) Yuri Slonimskii, *Reminiscences on the Dance,* Moscow, 1968; (7) Vera Krasovska, ed., *Soviet Ballet Theatre Materials 1917-1967,* 1976, (8) P. Karp, *On the Ballet,* Moscow, 1967; (9) Vera Krasovska, *Articles on the Ballet,* 1967; (10) Viktor Vanslov, *Ballets by Grigorovich and Problems of Their Choreography,* Moscow, 1968

All printed in Russian

Octavo, various sizes and bindings
Good condition; most illustrated   (10 in lot)

GEORGE GROSZ

■ 177   HINTERGRUND: *17 zeichnungen zur aufführung des "Schweijk" in der piscator-bühne,* Berlin, Malik-Verlag, 1928

Portfolio, oblong folio
Original wrappers, worn
Plates in good condition

ALEXANDRA EXTER

■ 178   Designs for a book
One page and one folio with illustration and text in gouache and two pages on tracing paper; one with text and one with illustrations in pencil
One signed; both stamped with the Estate stamp
one 1952 and the other 1975, and signed by Simon Lissim

From a very limited edition executed between 1930 and 1940

178

■ 179   COMOEDIA ILLUSTRE; Six copies, June 1, 1910; June 15, 1910; May 1, 1911; June 20, 1913; May 20, 1914 and June 5, 1914

Good condition apart from 2 pages cut in May 1, 1911 issue and some foxing in June 20, 1913 issue   (6 in lot)

■ 180   SERGE DE DIAGHILEFF BALLET RUSSE, SOUVENIR PROGRAM; Metropolitan Ballet Company, Inc., New York, 1916; photographic illustrations, some colored, after Bakst, within decorative borders, sewn into original gilt-decorated wrapper

together with

BALLETS RUSSE PROGRAMME OFFICIEL, Théâtre National de l'Opéra, Paris, December 29, 1915 (for the benefit of the British Red Cross); photographic illustrations, some colored, after Bakst within decorative borders; cover illustration by M. Larionov

and

THEATRE SARAH BERNHARDT GRANDE SAISON RUSSE; Paris, May-June, 1911, illustrated with photographs of the performers

and

FOLIES-BERGÈRE, Souvenir program (*circa* 1925); illustrated with photographs of the performers and with photographic illustrations some colored, after Erté, Brunelleschi, Barbier and others (4 in lot)

END OF SALE

Sotheby Parke Bernet Inc.

980 Madison Avenue

New York, N. Y. 10021

Bid Department 212 472-3435, 3436, 3450

Estimates (U. S. $)

DANCE · THEATER · OPERA · MUSIC HALL
SALE No. 4510M
THURSDAY, DECEMBER 18, 1980
AT MADISON AVENUE GALLERIES

NOTE: As a convenience to its clients, Sotheby Parke Bernet Inc. furnishes pre-sale estimates for all property included in the auctions. These estimates are our approximate valuations based, whenever possible, on comparable auction values excluding the 10% premium.

As provided for in the "Conditions of Sale" and as explained in the "Important Information For Prospective Bidders," all the property should be assumed to have reserves. In no case, where a reserve exists, will it exceed the range of estimates quoted below. A buyer's premium of 10% will be added to the successful bid price of each lot sold.

Lot	Estimate	Lot	Estimate	Lot	Estimate	Lot	Estimate	Lot	Estimate	Lot	Estimate
1	$250/350	33	$150/200	66	$500/800	99	$250/300	130	$5500/6500	162	$1000/1500
2	300/400	34	600/800	67	350/500	100	200/300	131	400/600	163	600/800
3	700/1000	35	300/500	68	1200/1600	101	200/300	132	500/700	164	400/600
4	300/400	36	100/150	69	700/900	102	600/800	133	500/700	165	200/300
5	300/400	37	800/1000	70	900/1200	103	200/300	134	2000/2500	166	700/900
6	500/700	38	600/800	71	350/500	104	400/600	135	2000/3000	167	700/900
7	150/200	39	500/700	72	600/800	105	300/400	136	3000/4000	168	400/600
8	200/250	40	200/300	73	500/700	106	300/400	137	300/500	169	500/600
9	300/500	41	100/150	74	600/800	107	300/500	138	500/800	170	150/200
10	2000/3000	42	50/100	75	600/800	108	150/200	139	3000/4000	171	400/600
11	1200/1600	43	300/500	76	600/800	109	2000/3000	140	1500/2000	172	350/450
12	500/700	44	500/800	77	600/800	110	1000/1500	141	5000/7000	173	100/150
12A	500/700	45	700/900	78	350/500	111	600/800	142	200/300	174	100/200
13	6000/8000	46	700/900	79	200/400	112	400/600	143	1000/1200	175	800/1200
14	900/1200	47	700/900	80	500/700	113	600/800	144	600/800	176	100/150
15	1000/1500	48	900/1200	81	300/500	114	1000/1500	144A	500/700	177	700/900
16	800/1000	49	400/600	82	400/600	115	500/700	145	300/500	178	400/500
17	600/900	50	400/600	83	300/500	116	700/1000	146	1000/1200	179	200/250
18	700/900	50A	140/180	84	1800/2200	117	700/900	147	1000/1500	180	100/150
19	6000/8000	51	700/1000	85	1200/1600	118	300/400	148	800/1000		
20	1500/2000	52	600/800	86	12,000/16,000	119	250/350	149	800/1000		
21	6000/8000	53	2500/3500	87	2500/3500	120	700/900	150	800/1000		
22	600/800	54	400/600	88	600/800	121	2000/3000	151	300/500		
23	3000/4000	55	2500/3500	89	500/700	122	8000/10,000	152	900/1200		
24	600/800	56	6000/8000	90	1500/2000	122A	1000/1500	153	4500/5500		
25	200/300	57	1800/2500	91	1000/1500	122B	1000/1500	154	200/400		
26	600/800	58	1200/1600	92	800/1000	123	2000/2500	155	120/150		
27	400/500	59	600/800	92A	800/1000	123A	4000/6000	156	600/800		
28	700/1000	60	600/800	93	500/700	124	4500/5500	157	7000/10,000		
29	700/900	61	600/800	94	500/800	125	4000/5000	158	2000/2500		
30	400/600	62	800/1000	95	1500/2000	126	5500/6500	158A	200/300		
31	300/400	63	700/1000	96	500/800	127	5500/6500	159	250/350		
31A	2500/3500	64	200/250	97	700/1000	128	5500/6500	160	600/800		
32	200/300	65	400/600	98	1500/2000	129	5500/6500	161	800/1000		

SALE 4510M
(Madison Avenue Galleries)

SOTHEBY PARKE BERNET INC.　　　　　　　　　Date _____

980 Madison Avenue
New York, N. Y. 10021
Bid Department (212) 472-3435, 3436, 3450

I desire to place the following bids for Sale #4510M to be held on December 18, 1980. These bids are to be executed by Sotheby Parke Bernet up to but not exceeding the amount or amounts specified below. Each bid is *PER LOT*, as indicated, and all bids will be executed and are accepted subject to the *"Conditions of Sale"* and *"Terms of Guarantee"* printed in the catalogue of this sale. **Please see *"Advice to Order Bidders"* on reverse of this bid slip and note that a premium of 10% will be added to the hammer price as part of the total purchase price.**

Name _____
　　　　(please print or type)

Address _____
　　　　　(Street)　　　　　　　　　　　　　　　　　　　　　　　　　　　(Apt.)

_____
　　　　　(City)　　　　　　　　　　　(State)　　　　　　　　　(Zip)

Telephone _____

Signed _____

Bank reference or deposit _____
　　　　　　　(If bidder is not known to Sotheby Parke Bernet Inc.)

Lot Number	Item	Top limit of Bid *not* including 10% premium (Bid is per lot number as listed in the catalogue) $

If Dealer, please give resale number _____ State _____

IMPORTANT: To facilitate handling, kindly mark envelope: *"Attention—Bid Department."*

BS 1/79

ADVICE TO ORDER BIDDERS

If instructed, Sotheby Parke Bernet Inc. will execute bids and advise prospective purchasers. This service is free. Lots will always be bought as cheaply as is allowed by such other bids and reserves as are on our books or bids executed in competition from the audience.

Please Note: Sotheby Parke Bernet Inc. offers this service as a convenience to its clients who are unable to attend the sale and will not be held responsible for error or failure to execute bids. Commission bids, when placed by telephone, are accepted only at the sender's risk, and must be confirmed by letter or telegram (Cable address: PARKGAL, NEW YORK).

Please use the bidding slips provided and be sure to carefully note lot numbers and descriptions.

Always quote the sale number of the catalogue to avoid any possible confusion.

Please bid as early as possible. In the event of identical bids, the earliest will take precedence.

"Buy" bids are not accepted. The limit you leave should be the amount to which you would bid if you were to attend the sale. Each bidding slip should contain bids for one sale only.

Alternative bids can be placed by using the "OR" between lot numbers.

In order to avoid delay in clearing purchases, buyers unknown to us are advised to make arrangements *before the sale* for payment or for references to be supplied. If such arrangements are not made, checks will be cleared before purchases are delivered.

IMPORTANT NOTE: Successful bidders will be notified and invoiced within a few days of the sale.

Unsuccessful bidders will not be specifically notified, but will receive a price list indicating results of the sale if a stamped, self-addressed envelope is enclosed with the submitted bid.

Your bid is for the hammer price; a premium of 10% will be added to the hammer price of each lot sold and is payable by you in addition thereto.

AB 1/79

Photographs by
Ed Spiro
SOTHEBY'S PHOTOGRAPHY DEPT.
(212) 472-3527

Consultant Art Director
ALAN HARTWELL, N.Y.C.

Separations by
TOPPAN PRINTING CO.

Printed in U.S.A. by
DANBURY PRINTING & LITHO, INC.

(070809)